MathLand®

Journeys Through Mathematics

Charles • Randolph Brummett • McDonald • Westley

DAILY TUNE-UPS

GRADE
4

Creative Publications®
Mountain View, CA

Contributing Writers • Ann Roper, Susan Alldredge
Project Editor • Cynthia Reak

Art Director • Violeta Diaz
Designer • Sharon Spurlock
Production Coordinator • Kate Rapson
Production Services • Morgan-Cain & Associates

Second Edition
©1998 Creative Publications
1300 Villa Street
Mountain View, California 94041

First Edition ©1995 Creative Publications
Printed in the United States of America.

ISBN: 0-7622-0301-3

1 2 3 4 5 6 7 8 9 10. 00 99 98

What are the Daily Tune-Ups?

The Daily Tune-Ups are 170 short, teacher-led math activities, one for each day of the typical school year.

Why are the Daily Tune-Ups important?

As educators become more and more influenced by the *NCTM Curriculum and Evaluation Standards for School Mathematics,* classrooms are moving toward project-based mathematics, where students are encouraged to construct mathematical meanings through in-depth investigations, such as those found in the *MathLand Guidebook.* This is an exciting and productive way for students to learn. However, students need a variety of experiences and formats to construct a holistic and broadly interconnected knowledge of mathematics.

The *Daily Tune-Ups* provide a format of short, frequent practice experiences that reinforce students' number sense, as well as the skills, symbols, and terminology important at each grade level. The activities in this collection help students master the tools they need to support their higher-level mathematical reasoning. Students need daily opportunities to think about and manipulate numbers in different contexts, to communicate their thinking, and to learn and use important conventions of mathematical language.

Both daily practice and open-ended explorations are vital elements of a well-rounded mathematics program. Thus, the *Daily Tune-Ups* are not intended to stand alone as a mathematics curriculum; instead, they are an important part of a comprehensive program that provides for problem solving and investigation of mathematical ideas over time.

How do I use the Daily Tune-Ups?

These whole-class activities can be done at any time of the day: first thing in the morning, just before lunch, or at the beginning of your math time. Choose a time that works best for you, and make it part of your daily routine.

A *Daily Tune-Up* takes 10-20 minutes. On one day, your class might spend a short time practicing counting by large numbers, while on another day, you might spend 20 minutes discussing students' mental computation strategies. Many *Tune-Ups* offer a selection of problems, and you may choose to present one, some, or all of the problems, or similar problems of your own, depending on where your students are mathematically, their level of engagement, and the time you have.

How do I integrate the Daily Tune-Ups into my mathematics curriculum?

The *Daily Tune-Ups* are an integral part of the *MathLand* program. They have been carefully sequenced to support the skills and language necessary in the investigations. The correlation chart on pages T14 and T15 shows which content areas are addressed in *Daily Tune-Ups* simultaneous to each *Guidebook* unit. The *Daily Tune-Ups* coordinated with each unit are also listed on the "Where We Are Going" pages in the *Guidebook*.

If you are using another mathematics program, the *Daily Tune-Ups* can be a powerful enhancement. The *Tune-Ups* deal with important mathematical content at each grade level and can fit easily into any program. The chart on pages T16 to T19 will help you to select the *Tune-Ups* appropriate to the area of mathematics your class is exploring.

How are the Daily Tune-Ups organized?

The Grade Four *Daily Tune-Ups* provide practice in twelve content areas:

Patterns	Place value
Counting	Mental arithmetic
Number recognition	Number facts
Sequencing numbers	Estimation
Fractions	Measurement
Problems	Geometry

The *Tune-Ups* are sequenced so students visit each content area regularly as they make their way through the book. Students build on prior knowledge in particular content areas and deepen their understanding of numbers. The activities gradually increase in complexity over the year.

What is the "Convince Me!" component of Daily Tune-Ups?

"Convince Me!" activities in the *Daily Tune-Ups* are a powerful means for developing students' number sense and communication. Students use their own methods to solve computation problems, and they explain and defend their strategies with each other. "Convince Me!" problems have one correct answer that students must find and defend based on sound mathematical reasoning. The "Convince Me!" approach is discussed in detail on pages T6 to T12.

Once the "Convince Me!" approach is introduced in the *MathLand Guidebook,* students have two to three "Convince Me!" experiences per week in the *Daily Tune-Ups* program.

How can I maximize children's learning and participation in the Daily Tune-Ups?

- When presenting an activity, think about open-ended questions you can ask, rather than statements that "tell." See "Teacher as Facilitator," page T9, for more on questioning.

- Use adequate wait time (no less than 3 seconds) before asking students to respond. During wait time, all hands should be down while students think quietly to themselves. Wait time has been shown to increase student participation and thoughtfulness. It downplays the belief that "fastest is best," a belief that discourages many students in math. Although it may feel awkward at first, students quickly come to expect that quiet "think time" prior to discussion.

- Mark the end of wait time by using a signal or saying, ***"Let's hear what you're thinking."***

- Promote 100% participation by having students discuss their thinking in partners prior to sharing out as a class. Pairs can also join in groups of four to discuss their thinking, then report as a group to the class.

- Support students who have difficulty with a *Tune-Up* by exploring similar problems with them in a small group. If a *Tune-Up* seems too challenging for most students, mark it and revisit it later in the year.

- Extend students' thinking about a *Daily Tune-Ups* activity by asking them to suggest similar problems of their own for the class to solve. Students may lead some of the activities with the class as well.

How is assessment built into the Daily Tune-Ups?

The *Daily Tune-Ups* offer frequent opportunities for ongoing student assessment which will: (1) provide information to you about your students' thinking, and (2) inform your decisions about further instruction.

Observation: Periodically focus on the responses of three or four students as you do an activity, or take several students aside to try an activity separate from the class. Carefully observe students' thinking, use of numbers, communication, and disposition, and keep a record of your observations if possible. Ask yourself questions, such as: *How clearly does [Maria] verbalize her thinking strategy? Does each step of the strategy lead logically to the next? Does she demonstrate a sense of numbers as quantities? What mathematical language or conventions is she using? Does she persevere or give up quickly?*

Writing: Keep a record of how students' number sense is developing by regularly having them write down their mental computation strategies to "Convince Me!" problems in lieu of the usual "Convince Me!" discussion. These pieces of writing can reveal areas of growth and difficulty in students' number sense and in their ability to communicate clearly in writing.

Reviews: A short review appears every 20 pages in the *Daily Tune-Ups*. These will help you check in on students' comfort level with the previous activities and their understanding in different content areas. Present review questions one at a time to the class. Use the overhead projector to present questions having bracketed instructions. Have students write their responses individually on a sheet of paper. Reproducible versions of each review are also provided in the *MathLand Resource Manager*, if you prefer to copy the review for your class.

Convince Me!

Solving Computation Problems with Mental Arithmetic

What is a "Convince Me!" discussion?

The "Convince Me!" approach for computational problem-solving is a unique alternative to traditional arithmetic programs in that students use **reasoning and discourse, rather than memorized algorithms,** to solve number problems. The problems have been carefully designed to encourage mental computation strategies rather than reliance on paper-and-pencil methods. Through discussion, students examine and judge the reasonableness of their answers based on what makes sense mathematically. This approach grows out of the belief that students construct a deep and flexible understanding of numbers through active reasoning and communication, rather than through memorization of rules.

"The major objective of elementary school mathematics should be to develop number sense. . . . It is not mindlessly mechanical, but flexible and synthetic in attitude. [It] includes common sense about how to find an answer as well as a range of choices of methods."

Everybody Counts: A Report to the Nation on the Future of Mathematics Education

Why a reasoning-based approach to numbers?

"Convince Me!" capitalizes on students' intuitive knowledge of the number system and their natural inclination to make sense of the world. Because numbers lie in logical and infinitely repeating patterns, students can rely on the power of their own reasoning to solve problems accurately. When students realize that the "rightness" and "wrongness" lie inherently within the numbers, they learn to rely on the authority of their own thinking.

In a reasoning-based approach, students use their developing algorithmic thinking to come up with their own procedures to find accurate solutions to number problems. Instead of memorizing rules for standard algorithms (for example, "start in the ones" and "borrow from the tens if you don't have enough ones"), students develop their own methods based on what makes sense mathematically. This approach is supported by research showing that students who are not taught standard algorithms rarely "start with the ones" when computing multi-digit numbers. Instead, they tend to work from left to right, dealing with larger parts of numbers first (like the hundreds in a 3-digit number). This suggests that children's natural tendency might be to view numbers as wholes, as distinct quantities, rather than a collection of digits in different "places."

When math instruction opposes students' natural reasoning processes, students can give up their emerging number sense in favor of following rules. Over time they may come to believe that they lack the innate ability to truly understand mathematics. The "Convince Me!" approach is based on the premise that *all* students can make sense of mathematics and become flexible, efficient, and accurate problem solvers.

How do I use "Convince Me!" in my classroom?

- Say a problem aloud as you write it on the board. Allow quiet wait time for the children to think. Students may write their answer and any "thinking notes" on their Miniboards. Let them know no hands should go up until you ask for answers. For further discussion about wait time, see page T4.

- Call on volunteers to give their answers. Record all answers on the board. At this time, you and the students should refrain from indicating whether or not answers are correct.

- Ask children to explain how they solved the problem while you record their thinking on the board. (See "Sample of a 'Convince Me!' Discussion," page T10.) Try to represent as closely as possible what students say. This will help the class follow students' thinking.

- Facilitate an exchange of ideas about proposed solutions requesting that children "convince" each other of their thinking, justifying the solutions offered. Children's arguments should rely on number sense and reasoning.

- Ask for several different explanations for the problem in question. *Are you convinced this solution is correct? Did someone solve this problem another way?* Help students discover and examine errors in their thinking with questions like *Could both of these solutions be correct? Why or why not?*

- By asking probing questions and by refraining from giving your own opinion about strategies or solutions, you can encourage students to rely on their own mathematical reasoning rather than on you to know when an answer is correct. Continually encourage students to refer to the numbers and emphasize reasonableness, efficiency, and accuracy.

Teacher as Facilitator

In "Convince Me!" discussions, the teacher: (1) asks open-ended questions that get children talking to each other, and (2) creates a class environment that supports risk-taking and interaction.

Open-Ended Questioning

"How," "why," and "what" questions are more effective than "yes/no" questions for eliciting opinions, reasoning, and debate. Some examples include:

- *How do you know?*
- *Why does this make sense?*
- *Who solved the problem in a different way? Explain.*
- *What questions do you have for [Alicia]?*
- *How did your partner solve the problem?*
- *Which strategy might you use if you were in a hurry? Why?*
- *What made you change your mind?*
- *Could both solutions be correct? Why or why not?*

The *Daily Tune-Up*s bookmark lists other effective open-ended questions.

Supportive Classroom Climate

Children need to know that they can speak up and make mistakes without feeling embarrassed. Build a supportive classroom environment by modeling a genuine curiosity about numbers and about children's thinking. If you ask children authentic questions about their reasoning, they are likely to tell you what they really think rather than what they think you want to hear. Provide many opportunities for children to get to know each other, and take time prior to and following collaborative activities for partners to discuss their social interactions.

A safe classroom climate is established over time. What feels safe to one student may not feel safe to another. If children are uncomfortable speaking up in class, provide other ways for them to show their thinking (writing, partner talk, signaling, etc.).

Sample of a "Convince Me!"
Discussion: 26 × 6 = ___

Teacher: Let's hear how you solved this problem mentally.

Elisa: I know that 20 times 6 is 120. And 6 times 6 is 36. 120 plus 36 is 156.

Teacher: [to class] Does Elisa's way make sense? Who solved this problem another way?

Carlos: I turned 26 into 25, and I did 25 six times and I got 150. But it's 26 six times, so I added 6 to 150 and got 156.

Teacher: Convince us that 25 six times is 150.

Carlos: 25 four times is 100, and two more 25s is 150.

Teacher: [to class] Are you convinced that 26 x 6 =156?

Class: [indicates agreement]

26 x 6 = ____

20 x 6 = 120
6 x 6 = 36
120 + 36 = 156

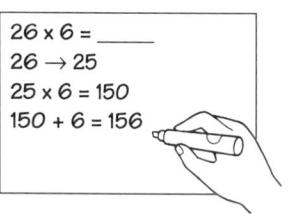

26 x 6 = ____
26 → 25
25 x 6 = 150
150 + 6 = 156

Teacher: How can we use Carlos' strategy to solve 24 x 9? Talk to your partner about that.

Ben: Well, Lee and I just turned 24 into 25, and we turned 9 into 10. Because those numbers are easier. So we did 25 x 10 = 250. And then we . . . wait . . .

$$24 \times 9 = \underline{\hspace{1cm}}$$
$$24 \to 25$$
$$9 \to 10$$
$$250 \times 10 = 250$$

Teacher: [to Ben and Lee] Can we ask you some questions? [to class] What questions do you have about this strategy?

Jackie: Well, if you change both numbers it gets confusing, because you lose track of what you multiplied by what. If you just kept 24 and multiplied that by 10, you would only need to take away one of the 24s, and you'd be done.

Lee: Okay, so that would be 240 - 20, which is 220, then take away 4 more and that's 216.

$$24 \times 9 = \underline{\hspace{1cm}}$$
$$24 \times 10 = 240$$
$$240 - 20 = 220$$
$$220 - 4 = 216$$

Teacher: Could we get the same answer if we rounded 24 to 25 and multiplied by 9?

Questions Teachers Ask About "Convince Me!"

Some of my students have been taught standard algorithms, and now they resist thinking about numbers in any other way. How can I work effectively with them?

Without negating their learned technique, encourage students to come up with multiple methods for solving problems and to use sound reasoning in their explanations. A helpful question might be, *"Is there another way to solve this problem besides starting in the ones?"* Having partners listen to and explain each other's strategies might also help students break out of limited ways of thinking.

How can I help students who have trouble getting started?

If students are unable to take the first step to solving a problem, try asking questions about the numbers they are working with, like *"What do you know about this number? Is it close to any other number that is easy for you to think about?"* Questions that elicit estimation can also help children access their number sense; for example, *"Do you think the answer will be more or less than 100? Why?"*

How will this approach help to prepare my students for standardized tests?

"Convince Me!" helps students to develop accurate, efficient methods for solving number problems like those that appear on standardized tests. Building students' number sense supports their ability to detect errors and to judge the reasonableness of answers. Students become familiar with wording on standardized test problems by encountering similar wording in *Daily Tune-Ups* reviews.

Daily Tune-Ups Materials

If you are using the MathLand Guidebook, the materials listed below can be found in the Overhead Kit, the Classroom Kit, and the Consumable Kit.

Overhead Materials

Coins

0-9 Numeral Tiles

Fraction Circles PLUS™

Base Ten Blocks

Inch/Centimeter Ruler

Manipulative Materials

Rainbow Cubes

Polygon Tiles

Fraction Circles PLUS™

Consumable Materials

Miniboards

Daily Tune-Ups Correlation

	MathLand Guidebook			Daily Tune-Ups	Patterns	Counting	Number Recognition	Sequencing Numbers	Fractions	Place Value	Mental Arithmetic	Number Facts	Estimation	Measurement	Geometry	Problems
Unit	**wk**	**pages**	**Investigation Focus**													
Unit #1	1	6-13	Organizing Data	1-5		•	•	•		•		•				
All About Us	2	14-21	Designing Surveys	6-10	•		•		•			•	•			
Unit #2	1	30-37	Geometric Patterns	11-15	•			•		•		•				
Looking for Rules	2	38-45	Number Patterns	16-20	•	•			•					•		
Unit #3	1	54-61	Multiplication	21-25			•		•	•			•	•		
Strategies	2	62-69	Memorization	26-30					•	•	•					•
	3	70-77	Mental Strategies	31-35			•				•		•			•
	4	78-85	Using Calculators	36-40	•						•			•		
	5	86-93	Number Strategies	41-45		•				•				•		
Unit #4	1	102-109	Analyzing Attributes	46-50						•		•	•	•		
Examining	2	110-117	Logical Thinking	51-55							•	•				
Differences and																
Possibilities																
Unit #5	1	126-133	Fraction Relationships	56-60	•		•					•				
Numbers	2	134-141	Fraction Circles	61-65				•				•				•
Between	3	142-149	Equivalence	66-70					•			•				
Numbers	4	150-157	Adding and Subtracting	71-75								•		•		
	5	158-165	Fraction Problems	76-80		•						•	•			

	Daily Tune-Ups Correlation																
MathLand Guidebook																	
Unit	wk	pages	Investigation Focus	Daily Tune-Ups	Patterns	Counting	Number Recognition	Sequencing Numbers	Fractions	Place Value	Mental Arithmetic	Number Facts	Estimation	Measurement	Geometry	Problems
Unit #6	1	174-181	Exploring Area	81-85				•			•					•
Spaces	2	182-189	Area and Perimeter	86-90					•		•			•		
	3	190-197	Measuring Area	91-95					•	•	•		•	•		
Unit #7	1	206-213	Squares and Cubes	96-100					•		•			•		
Representations	2	214-221	Modeling Numbers	101-105					•		•					•
	3	222-229	Multiplication	106-110				•	•		•			•		
	4	230-237	Prices and Profits	111-115					•		•		•	•		
	5	238-245	Estimation	116-120						•	•					
Unit #8	1	254-261	Visual Thinking	121-125				•	•		•	•				
Shaping	2	262-269	Classifying Shapes	126-130					•		•					•
Relationships	3	270-277	Relationships	131-135				•	•	•	•					
Unit #9	1	286-293	Data Analysis	136-140			•				•				•	
Dinosaur	2	294-301	Scale Drawings	141-145					•		•				•	
Days	3	302-309	Measurement	146-150						•	•					•
	4	310-317	Comparisons	151-155				•	•		•	•				
	5	318-325	Solving Problems	156-160					•		•				•	
Unit #10	1	334-341	Exploring Probability	161-165					•		•					•
'Round They Go	2	342-349	Designing Games	166-170					•		•					•

Daily Tune-Ups

Fractions
7 Point It Out!
17 Name That Fraction!
25 Show Me!
26 Name That Piece!
50 Draw Me!
69 Name That Piece!
87 Imagine This!
88 What's Half?
91 Convince Me!
96 What's Half?
97 Imagine This!
105 How Many Halves?
108 Convince Me!
109 Two Names for One
113 Convince Me!

Fractions
124 True or False?
125 Convince Me!
127 Convince Me!
131 Convince Me!
135 Convince Me!
141 Two Names for One
142 What Could They Be?
145 Convince Me!
151 Convince Me!
155 Convince Me!
156 Is It Greater?
162 What Could They Be?

Number recognition
1 Name That Number
6 Write It Down!
34 Name That Number
57 Name That Number
79 Write It Down!
138 Write It Down!

Number facts
2 Which Divide Evenly?
12 Which One Is Different?
54 Times Tables
77 Multiplying Coins
121 Times Tables
154 Which Divide Evenly?

Mental arithmetic
9 Listen and Think
27 Missing Signs
30 They're Connected!
37 Convince Me!
39 Convince Me!
43 Convince Me!
45 Convince Me!
47 Convince Me!
51 Convince Me!
52 They're Connected!
53 Convince Me!
55 Convince Me!
56 Listen and Think
58 Convince Me!
61 Convince Me!
63 Convince Me!
65 Convince Me!
66 Convince Me!
67 Convince Me!
68 Convince Me!

Mental arithmetic
72 Convince Me!
73 Listen and Think
74 Story Math
75 Convince Me!
76 Convince Me!
78 Convince Me!
81 Convince Me!
83 Convince Me!
85 Convince Me!
86 Convince Me!
89 Convince Me!
93 Convince Me!
98 Convince Me!
101 Convince Me!
102 How Much?
103 Convince Me!
111 Convince Me!
115 Convince Me!
116 How Much Is Hidden?
117 Missing Signs

Mental arithmetic
118 Convince Me!
123 Convince Me!
126 Listen and Think
128 How Much?
129 Convince Me!
133 Convince Me!
137 Convince Me!
139 Convince Me!
143 Convince Me!
146 How Much Is Hidden?
149 Convince Me!
157 Convince Me!
159 Convince Me!
161 Convince Me!
163 Convince Me!
165 Convince Me!
167 Convince Me!
169 Convince Me!

Place value
4 1000 More
14 You Make the Number
23 What's the Greatest?
28 Millions and Millions
33 1000 More
38 Billions and Millions
94 Billions and Millions
119 Billions and Millions
132 10,000 More
148 Billions and Millions

Sequencing numbers
5 What Comes After?
15 What Comes Before?
42 True or False?
64 What Comes Between?
84 On the Nose!
107 Greater Than, Less Than
122 What's Missing?
134 Write It Right
152 Write It Right
166 What Comes Before?

Measurement
19 Money Matters
21 Measure Up
41 Money Matters
48 Measure Up
49 Convince Me!
70 Convince Me!
71 Measure Up
90 Measure Up
95 How Much Time?
99 Money Matters
106 Convince Me!
110 Measure Up
114 How Long?
147 Convince Me!
153 Convince Me!
158 How Long?

Name That Number

Let's name some big numbers. I'll write some numbers here on the overhead projector and you say their names with me. Ready? Write the following numbers one at a time, naming each one with the students after you write it.

Try these:

- 3305; 4219; 1269

- 5384; 8778; 6578

- 2943; 9012; 7166

3305

2 Which Divide Evenly?

It's a Miniboard day! Look at these division equations. Write them on your Miniboards. Then raise your hand when you find the equation that has an answer with a remainder. We'll all say that equation together. Write on the overhead projector:
25 ÷ 5 = _____; 24 ÷ 8 = _____; 27 ÷ 3 = _____;
15 ÷ 4 = _____. Give the students time to think about the
equations, and wait until most have raised their hands. (**15 ÷ 4**)

Repeat with the following equations: 36 ÷ 12 = _____;
30 ÷ 5 = _____; 24 ÷ 5 = _____; 20 ÷ 4 = _____.
(**24 ÷ 5**)

Topic: Number facts   **Focus:** Division   MathLand®: Grade Four
© Creative Publications **2**

Let's Count!

Let's count forward from 10,235 to 10,240 and then backward to 10,232. We'll count all together. Ready? Begin: 10,235; 10,236; ...

Now let's count forward from 15,498 to 15,510 and then backward to 15,000. Ready? Begin: 15,498; 15,499; ...

15,498; 15,499; 15,500 . . .

Topic: Counting   **Focus:** Counting forward and back

MathLand®: Grade Four
© Creative Publications

4 1000 More

It's a Miniboard day! You're going to write the number that is 1000 more than the number I write. Write a number on the overhead projector. *On your Miniboards write the number that is 1000 more than this one.* On your signal, have the class show their Miniboards.

Try these:

- 1010; 3200; 2009 (**2010; 4200; 3009**)

- 8765; 9431; 7173 (**9765; 10,431; 8173**)

- 5110; 6370; 4028 (**6110; 7370; 5028**)

For a challenge, have the class write the numbers that are 1000 less than the numbers you write.

5 What Comes After?

Let's play the **What Comes After?** *game. I'll say a number and then you say the number that comes after it.* Say random numbers from 1 to 9999 and have the class say the next number.

Try these:

- **3223** (3224)

- **8781** (8782)

- **9989** (9990)

◇ 6 ◇ **Write It Down!**

It's a Miniboard day! Let's practice writing some numbers.
I'll say some numbers and you write them on your Miniboards.
Ready? Say the following numbers slowly, giving the students
time to write them. On your signal, the students should hold up
their Miniboards.

Try these:

- 2124; 4205; 1346

- 7438; 3539; 5667

- 9702; 5893; 6961

Topic: Number recognition, greater than 1000   **Focus:** Writing numbers

7 Point It Out!

Let's practice finding fractions. One row at a time, write the following fractions on the chalkboard. Spread them out as much as possible. Name one of the fractions in each row, and ask the class to point to it.

Try these:

- $\frac{2}{3}$ $\frac{1}{2}$ $\frac{2}{2}$ $\frac{1}{3}$ ***Point to*** $\frac{1}{2}$***.***

- $\frac{3}{4}$ $\frac{4}{4}$ $\frac{1}{2}$ $\frac{1}{4}$ ***Point to*** $\frac{1}{4}$***.***

- $\frac{2}{3}$ $\frac{3}{3}$ $\frac{1}{3}$ $\frac{3}{2}$ ***Point to*** $\frac{2}{3}$***.***

- $\frac{2}{3}$ $\frac{1}{2}$ $\frac{1}{3}$ $\frac{3}{3}$ ***Point to*** $\frac{1}{3}$***.***

- $\frac{3}{4}$ $\frac{4}{3}$ $\frac{2}{4}$ $\frac{1}{4}$ ***Point to*** $\frac{3}{4}$***.***

What Number Comes Next?

Ready for some pattern practice? I'll write a number pattern and you tell me what comes next. Write a number pattern on the overhead projector. Pause for two or three seconds and then have the students say the next number with you.

500

Try these:

• 100, 200, 300, 400, … **(500)**

• 15, 17, 19, 21, … **(23)**

• 3, 6, 9, 12, … **(15)**

Listen and Think

We're going to add and subtract some numbers in our heads. Listen closely, then we'll all say the answer together. Pause after saying the first two numbers, then continue with the last one. *Ready? 30 + 10 + 8.* Begin saying the problems slowly, but increase the pace as you progress. **(48)**

Try these:

- *10 + 20 − 5* **(25)**
- *6 + 4 − 9* **(1)**
- *9 + 50 − 8* **(51)**

10 That's Close Enough!

Write the following problems on the overhead projector one at a time. Turn the light on and off quickly after you write each one, then ask, ***About what should the answer be? Why did you choose that number? Tell us about your thinking.*** Encourage estimates, not exact answers. (**Exact answers are shown.**)

- $\begin{array}{r} 150 \\ +\ 47 \end{array}$ **(197)**

- $\begin{array}{r} 800 \\ +\ 132 \end{array}$ **(932)**

- $\begin{array}{r} 100 \\ -\ 68 \end{array}$ **(32)**

- $\begin{array}{r} 167 \\ -\ 29 \end{array}$ **(138)**

Counting Two-by-Two

Let's count out loud by twos from 12,000 to 12,020. We'll count together. Are you ready? Begin: 12,000; 12,002; 12,004; ...

Now let's count by twos from 15,990 to 16,010. Ready? Begin: 15,990; 15,992; ...

12,004; 12,006; 12,008 ...

Topic: Counting   **Focus:** Counting by twos

12 ◁▷ Which One Is Different?

Let's look here at the overhead projector. I'll write 4 multiplication equations on it. You look at them and raise your hand when you see the equation that has a different answer from the others. Then we'll all say that equation together. Write on the overhead projector: $8 \times 6 =$ _____; $24 \times 2 =$ _____; $12 \times 3 =$ _____; $4 \times 12 =$ _____. Give the students time to think about the equations, and wait until most of them have raised their hands. ($12 \times 3 =$ _____)

Try these:

- $8 \times 7 =$ _____; $20 \times 3 =$ _____; ($8 \times 7 =$ _____)
  $2 \times 30 =$ _____; $10 \times 6 =$ _____

- $40 \times 2 =$ _____; $10 \times 8 =$ _____; ($9 \times 9 =$ _____)
  $9 \times 9 =$ _____; $20 \times 4 =$ _____

Ready for some pattern practice? I'll write a number pattern and you tell me what comes next. Write a number pattern on the overhead projector. Pause for two or three seconds and then have the students say the next number with you.

Try these:

- 4, 8, 12, 16, … **(20)**

- 7, 14, 21, 28, … **(35)**

- 9, 18, 27, 36, … **(45)**

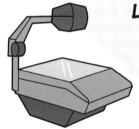

4, 8, 12, 16,

14   You Make the Number

It's a Miniboard day again! You're going to create some numbers. Turn on the overhead projector and put five transparent Numeral Tiles on it randomly. *I'd like you to write the greatest number possible, using these five numerals. Write it on your Miniboards.* On your signal, have the class show their Miniboards.

For a change, try the same activity having the students create the least numbers possible.

Try these:

					(greatest)	(least)
•	1	2	3	4	7	(74,321)	(12,347)
•	0	2	6	8	9	(98,620)	(02,689)
•	1	5	7	8	9	(98,751)	(15,789)

Topic: Place value   **Focus:** Creating numbers

15 ◇ What Comes Before?

Let's play the **What Comes Before?** *game. I'll say a number and then you say the number that comes just before it.* Say random numbers from 1 to 10,000 and have the class say the previous number.

Try these:

- *2427* (2426)

- *4681* (4680)

- *8360* (8359)

16 ◇ Counting by Threes

Let's count together by threes from 11,330 to 11,348. Ready? Here goes! 11,330; 11,333; 11,336; ...

Now let's count by threes from 33,333 to 33,351. Ready? Go! 33,333; 33,336; 33,339; ...

> 11,330; 11,333; 11,336 ...

Name That Fraction!

Let's practice naming fractions. Write $\frac{1}{2}$ on the overhead projector. Pause briefly, then have the class say the fraction name together. Continue writing other fractions and having the class name them together.

Try these:

- $\frac{1}{3}$
- $\frac{1}{4}$

- $\frac{4}{8}$
- $\frac{2}{3}$

- $\frac{3}{6}$
- $\frac{3}{5}$

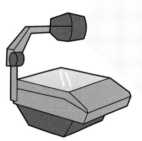

$$\frac{1}{2}$$

Topic: Fractions

Focus: Naming

MathLand®: Grade Four
© Creative Publications

It's Odd! and Even

Time for pattern practice! I'll write an odd-number pattern and you say what comes next. Write a number pattern on the overhead projector. Pause for two or three seconds and then have the students say the next number with you.

107, 109, 111 . . .

Try these:

- 101, 103, 105, 107, … **(109)**

- 75, 77, 79, 81, … **(83)**

Now let's try an even-number pattern.

Try these:

- 200, 202, 204, 206, … **(208)**

- 50, 52, 54, 56, 58, … **(60)**

Topic: Patterns   **Focus:** Following odd- and even-number patterns

Money Matters

Time to think about money, that is dollars and cents. I'll write some amounts of money on the overhead projector and we'll read them out loud together. Let's try the first one. Write $1.30 on the overhead and say with the students, *One dollar and thirty cents.* Write other amounts and say them with the class.

One dollar and thirty cents

Try these:

- 49¢, 73¢, 82¢

- $3.36, $5.17, $2.50

- $4.11, $10.00, $15.12

Answers

1. [Write: 55, 57, 59, 61] *Write the number that comes next.*   **63**

2. *Write the number I say: Three thousand, five hundred thirty-nine.*   **3539**

3. [Write: 7360] *Write the number that comes before.*   **7359**

4. *Write the fraction I say:* $\frac{3}{5}$ $\frac{3}{5}$

5. [Numeral Tiles: 0, 1, 3, 7, 9] *Using these numerals, write the greatest number possible.*   **97,310**

6. *Add these numbers in your head. Write the answer.* $40 + 10 + 7.$ **57**

7. [Write: $8 \times 5 =$ _____; $4 \times 12 =$ _____; $10 \times 4 =$ _____; $20 \times 2 =$ _____]
   Write the equation that has a different answer from the others. $4 \times 12 =$ _____

8. [Write: $140 + 37.$ Show quickly.] *Estimate the answer.*   **vary**

9. *Write the amount, $13.14, in dollars and cents.*   **$13.14**

For Verbal Response

10. *Count by twos from 14,000 to 14,020.*

21 ◇ Measure Up

Let's talk about measurement. Put a transparent inch ruler on the overhead projector. Draw a line that is exactly 3 inches long. Ask the students to read the ruler and tell how long the line is. Mark off other lines in inch lengths and have the class tell the lengths. Each time they name a length, write it by the line.

Counting Forward and Back

Let's try this way of counting. I'll write three numbers on the overhead projector. You start counting at the first number, count to the second number, and then count back to the third number. Count with the class a time or two and then let them try without you.

Try these:

- 11,517 … 11,526 … 11,518

- 14,789 … 14,797 … 14,790

- 18,964 … 18,972 … 18,962

11,517; 11,518; 11,519; 11,520; 11,521; 11,522 …

23 What's the Greatest?

It's a Miniboard day! I'll write three numbers on the overhead projector. You write them in order from least to greatest on your Miniboards. Turn on the overhead projector and write three numbers on it. On your signal, have the class show their Miniboards.

Try these:

- 1710; 1170; 1017

- 6325; 2356; 3256

- 1803; 3081; 8103

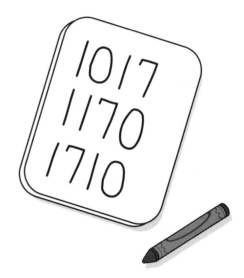

About How Many?

Today we'll look at some cubes and decide about how many, not exactly how many there are! Watch the overhead projector. Then I'll ask you some "more" or "fewer" questions. Ready? Put 35 Rainbow Cubes, arranged roughly in groups of 5, on the overhead stage. Turn on the light for a few seconds and then turn it off. Ask, ***Did you see more than 30 cubes? What do you think? Why do you think so?***

Repeat the activity with a slightly different number of cubes and ask the same questions.

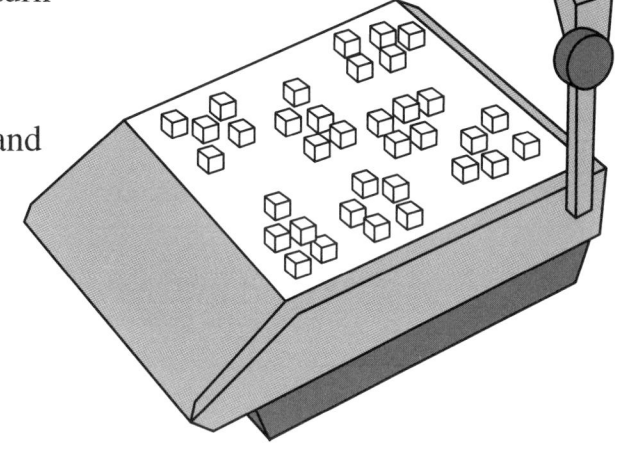

It's a Miniboard day! You're going to write fractions on your boards as I say them. Name the following fractions one at a time, and give the students time to write them. On your signal, the students should show their Miniboards.

Try these:

- $\frac{1}{4}$
- $\frac{3}{6}$
- $\frac{2}{3}$
- $\frac{4}{8}$

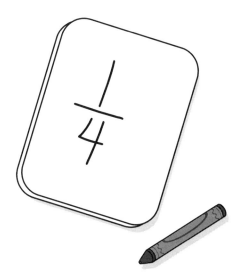

Topic: Fractions   **Focus:** Writing   MathLand®: Grade Four
© Creative Publications   **25**

Name That Piece!

Let's practice naming fractions by looking at the pieces. Use transparent Fraction Circles on the overhead projector to show different fractions. Put on the whole region with a $\frac{1}{3}$ piece on top of it. Turn on the light and say, ***Let's say the name of this fraction: one third.*** Continue covering the whole with other fraction pieces and having the students name them.

Try these:

- $\frac{3}{4}$
- $\frac{1}{10}$

- $\frac{2}{5}$
- $\frac{6}{8}$

- $\frac{2}{12}$
- $\frac{4}{10}$

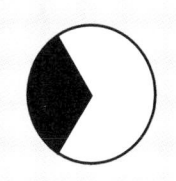

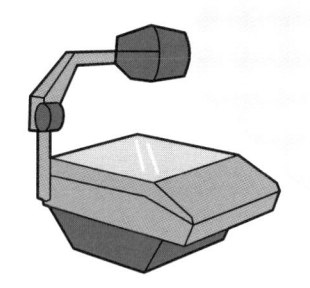

Missing Signs

It's another Miniboard day! Are you ready? I'm going to write an equation on the overhead projector. But I'll put circles where the operations signs go. You write the equation on your Miniboards and put in signs to make the equation correct. Work inside the parentheses first. Here we go! Write the following equations one at a time, and give the class enough time to copy them and write the signs. Then read the complete equations together.

Try these:

- $(7 \bigcirc 7) \bigcirc 2 = 51 \; (\times, +)$

- $(20 \bigcirc 16) \bigcirc 8 = 12 \; (-, +)$

- $(5 \bigcirc 1) \bigcirc 3 = 2 \; (\div, -)$

Topic: Mental arithmetic   **Focus:** Computing mentally

MathLand®: Grade Four
© Creative Publications

Millions and Millions

Prepare three index cards for this activity. On one card write Million; on one write Thousand, and leave the last one blank. Set the cards up in that order, left to right, in the chalktray. Above the Million card, write 347. Above the Thousand card, write 263, and above the blank card, write 125.

Time for something different! You're going to learn how to read numbers in the millions. After you read each group of three numbers, say the name that is on the card below them. Read with the class: ***Three hundred forty-seven million, two hundred sixty-three thousand, one hundred twenty-five.*** Let various students take turns saying the number by themselves.

Repeat, writing other three-digit numbers above the cards.

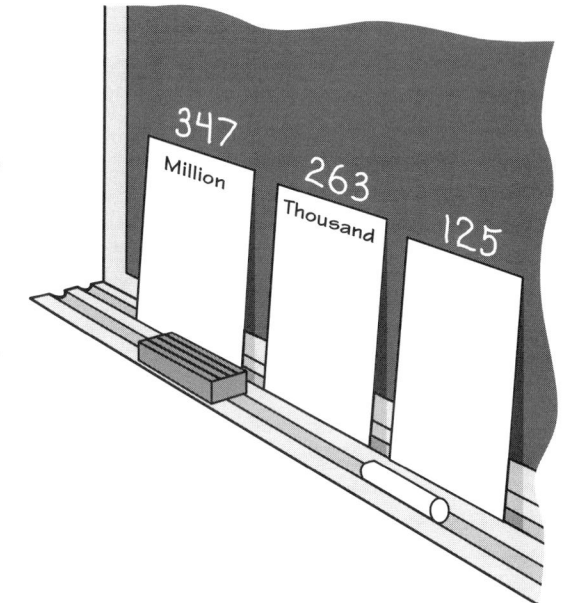

Say the Numbers

Today you're going to say the numbers shown by blocks. Put transparent Base Ten Blocks on the overhead projector to show the number 45. Ask the students to name the number the blocks show. Continue, showing other numbers with blocks.

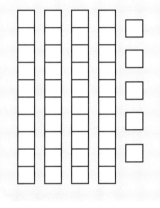

Try these:

- 3 tens blocks, 7 ones blocks

- 6 tens blocks, 2 ones blocks

- 1 hundreds block, 1 tens block, 6 ones blocks

- 1 hundreds block, 4 ones blocks

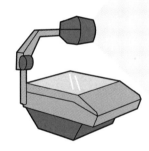

They're Connected!

*We're going to do some more math in our heads. Listen
closely, then we'll all say the answer together. Ready? 2 × 5.*
Wait a second, then say the answer with the students and
continue: *2 × 50 ... 2 × 500.*

Try these:

- *3 × 5, 3 × 50, 3 × 500* (15, 150, 1500)

- *6 × 5, 6 × 50, 6 × 500* (30, 300, 3000)

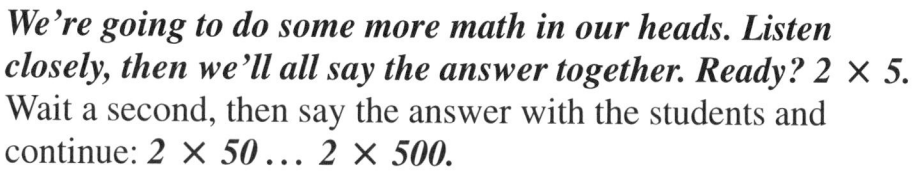

Topic: Mental arithmetic   **Focus:** Related multiplication

What's It Between?

Today we're going to do some estimating. I'll write an addition problem here on the overhead projector and give you a few seconds to look at it. Then I'll ask someone to tell us two numbers that the answer is between. Ready? Write 3257 + 6128 on the overhead, turn on the light for about 3 seconds, then turn it off. ***Let's name two numbers that the answer would fall between.*** See if anyone wants to narrow the range. Ask the students why they came up with those numbers. **(actual answer = 9385)**

Try these:

- 7423
  − 1278
  (6145)

- 10,342
  + 8768
  (19,110)

(Actual answers are shown.)

| **Topic:** Estimation | **Focus:** Finding a range for answers | MathLand®: Grade Four
© Creative Publications | **31** |

You Write It!

Today is a Miniboard day! You're going to write the numbers that the Base Ten Blocks show. Put transparent Base Ten Blocks on the overhead projector to show the number 33. *Look up here, then write on your Miniboards the number the blocks show.* On your signal, the class should show their Miniboards.

Try these:

- 2 tens blocks, 5 ones blocks **(25)**

- 1 hundreds block, 4 tens blocks, 1 ones block **(141)**

- 1 hundreds block, 2 tens blocks, 3 ones blocks **(123)**

- 2 hundreds blocks, 3 tens blocks **(230)**

33　1000 More

It's a Miniboard day! You're going to write the number that is 1000 more than the number I write. Turn on the overhead projector and write a number on it. ***Write on your Miniboards the number that is 1000 more than this one.*** On your signal, have the class show their Miniboards.

Try these:

- 14,310; 32,000; 28,700

- 18,476; 19,471; 17,174

- 51,011; 63,872; 30,248

For a challenge, have the class write the numbers that are 1000 less than the ones you write.

15,310
33,000
29,700

Name That Number

Let's practice naming big numbers. I'll write some numbers here on the overhead projector and you say their names with me. Ready? Write the following numbers one at a time, naming each one with the students after you write it.

Try these:

- 10,405; 46,219; 12,042

- 51,444; 17,778; 32,178

- 20,966; 29,067; 18,071

Ten thousand, four hundred five

Topic: Number recognition, greater than 10,000   **Focus:** Naming numbers

MathLand®: Grade Four
© Creative Publications

35 It's a Problem

Today is a Miniboard day! Put transparent Base Ten Blocks on the overhead projector to show 2 rows of 15. Turn on the light and say, **Look at these blocks and think of the addition problem they show. Write the equation that shows the problem and then write the answer.** On your signal, the students should show their Miniboards.

Try these:

• 2 rows with 13 in each row (**13 + 13 = 26**)

• 2 rows with 14 in each row (**14 + 14 = 28**)

Topic: Problems   **Focus:** Addition

Think Back

Ready for more pattern practice? Let's try counting backward in a pattern by threes. We'll start at 15. Say with the students, *15, 12, 9, ...*

15, 12, 9, 6 ...

Try these:

- 99, 96, 93, 90, ...

- 100, 97, 94, 91, ...

Convince Me!

Write the following problems on the chalkboard one at a time.
Engage the class in a Convince Me! discussion as explained on
pages T6 to T12.

- $\begin{array}{r} 10 \\ +\ \ 7 \end{array}$ **(17)**

- $13 + 9 =$ **(22)**

- $\begin{array}{r} 20 \\ -\ \ 8 \end{array}$ **(12)**

- $\begin{array}{r} 35 \\ -\ 10 \end{array}$ **(25)**

- $\begin{array}{r} 11 \\ +\ 14 \end{array}$ **(25)**

- $\begin{array}{r} 17 \\ +\ \ 8 \end{array}$ **(25)**

- $22 - 11 =$ **(11)**

- $\begin{array}{r} 36 \\ -\ 14 \end{array}$ **(22)**

Topic: Discussions

Focus: Computation strategies

38

Billions and Millions

Prepare four index cards for this activity. On one card write Billion; on one write Million; on one write Thousand, and leave the last one blank. Set the cards up in that order, left to right, in the chalktray. Above the Billion card, write 873. Above the Million card, write 906. Above the Thousand card, write 741, and above the blank card, write 521.

Today you're going to learn how to read numbers in the billions. After you read each group of three numbers, say the name that is on the card below them. Read with the class: ***Eight hundred seventy-three billion, nine hundred six million, seven hundred forty-one thousand, five hundred twenty-one.*** Let various students take turns saying the number by themselves.

Repeat, writing other three-digit numbers above the cards.

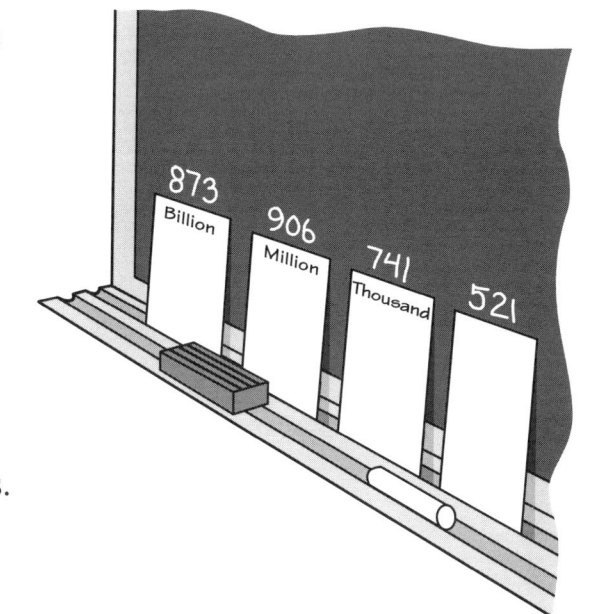

Topic: Place value   **Focus:** Learning period names

Convince Me!

Write the following problems on the chalkboard one at a time.
Engage the class in a Convince Me! discussion as explained on
pages T6 to T12.

- $\begin{array}{r} 12 \\ + 16 \end{array}$ **(28)**

- $\begin{array}{r} 18 \\ + 31 \end{array}$ **(49)**

- $\begin{array}{r} 43 \\ - 13 \end{array}$ **(30)**

- $\begin{array}{r} 66 \\ - 55 \end{array}$ **(11)**

- 35 + 7 = **(42)**

- $\begin{array}{r} 36 \\ + 6 \end{array}$ **(42)**

- $\begin{array}{r} 4 \\ \times 5 \end{array}$ **(20)**

- 5 × 5 = **(25)**

Topic: Discussions

Focus: Computation strategies

1. [Write: 60, 57, 54, 51, ____] *Write the number that comes next.* — 48
2. [Fraction Circles: whole with $\frac{1}{5}$ piece on top] *Name this fraction.* — $\frac{1}{5}$
3. [Write: 54,072] *Write the number that is one thousand greater.* — 55,072
4. [Write: 4325, 5324, 2534] *Write the numbers in order from least to greatest.* — 2534...5324
5. [Write: (6 ◯ 6) ◯ 3 = 33] *Write the signs to make that equation correct.* — $\times, -$
6. [Write: 4247 + 5138] *Write two numbers the answer falls between.* — vary
7. [Inch Ruler: Draw 5-inch line.] *How long is the line?* — 5 inches
8. [Base Ten Blocks: 2 rows of 16 each] *Write the addition problem shown.* — $16 + 16 = 32$
9. [Write: 40,702; 47,042; 47,402] *Write the number I say: 47,042.* — 47,042

For Verbal Response

10. [Write: 12,764...12,773...12,765] *Count forward, then backward.*

Let's think about money. I'll write some amounts of money on the overhead projector and you read them out loud. Write $1.38 on the overhead and say with the students, ***One dollar and thirty-eight cents***. Write other amounts and have the class read them aloud.

Try these:

- $0.67, $0.49, $0.07

- $1.35, $1.69, $8.72

- $6.15, $9.32, $64.98

One dollar and thirty-eight cents!

Topic: Measurement   **Focus:** Reading money notation

MathLand®: Grade Four
© Creative Publications

True or False?

Today we are going to think about greater than and less than.
Write 23 < 47 on the overhead projector with the light off. Turn
on the light and say, ***Look at this number statement. Let's read
it together, wait, and then say if it is true or false.*** Read it with
the students, pause, then say, ***True.*** Repeat the activity with
other statements, some true and some false.

23 is less
than 47 ...
TRUE!

Try these:

- 72 > 97 **(F)**

- 341 > 394 **(F)**

- 1601 < 1660 **(T)**

- 907 < 9007 **(T)**

- 7215 > 7251 **(F)**

43 Convince Me!

Write the following problems on the chalkboard one at a time. Engage the class in a Convince Me! discussion as explained on pages T6 to T12.

- 15 + 16 = **(31)**

-
  $$
  \begin{array}{r}
  68 \\
  -\ 13 \\
  \hline
  \end{array}
  $$
  (55)

-
  $$
  \begin{array}{r}
  6 \\
  \times\ 3 \\
  \hline
  \end{array}
  $$
  (18)

-
  $$
  \begin{array}{r}
  129 \\
  +\ \ 3 \\
  \hline
  \end{array}
  $$
  (132)

-
  $$
  \begin{array}{r}
  18 \\
  +\ 19 \\
  \hline
  \end{array}
  $$
  (37)

-
  $$
  \begin{array}{r}
  46 \\
  -\ 24 \\
  \hline
  \end{array}
  $$
  (22)

- 4 × 7 = **(28)**

-
  $$
  \begin{array}{r}
  137 \\
  +\ \ 4 \\
  \hline
  \end{array}
  $$
  (141)

Topic: Discussions   **Focus:** Computation strategies

MathLand® : Grade Four
© Creative Publications

44 ◇ Skip Counting

Let's practice skip counting. We'll count first by twenties up to 200. Ready? Go! 20, 40, 60, 80, ...

Try these:

- **By hundreds: 100, 200, 300, ...**

- **By thousands: 1000, 2000, 3000, ...**

- **By five thousands: 5000; 10,000; 15,000; ...**

400, 500, 600 ...

Convince Me!

Write the following problems on the chalkboard one at a time.
Engage the class in a Convince Me! discussion as explained on
pages T6 to T12.

- $\begin{array}{r} 25 \\ + 77 \\ \hline \end{array}$ **(102)**

- $\begin{array}{r} 65 \\ + 28 \\ \hline \end{array}$ **(93)**

- $3 \times 8 =$ **(24)**

- $26 \div 2 =$ **(13)**

- $\begin{array}{r} 12 \\ \times 5 \\ \hline \end{array}$ **(60)**

- $\begin{array}{r} 10 \\ \times 8 \\ \hline \end{array}$ **(80)**

- $\begin{array}{r} 65 \\ - 9 \\ \hline \end{array}$ **(56)**

- $\begin{array}{r} 78 \\ - 19 \\ \hline \end{array}$ **(59)**

Topic: Discussions   **Focus:** Computation strategies

What's It Between?

Today we're going to estimate. I'll write a subtraction problem here on the overhead projector and give you a few seconds to look at it. Then I'll ask someone to tell us two numbers that the answer is between. Ready? Write 5368 − 4219 on the overhead, turn on the light for about 3 seconds, then turn it off. *Let's name two numbers that the answer would fall between.* See if anyone wants to narrow the range. Ask the students why they came up with those numbers. **(actual answer: 1149)**

Try these:

- 3722
  − 1978

   (actual answer: 1744)

- 4039
  − 148

   (actual answer: 3891)

Convince Me!

Write the following problems on the chalkboard one at a time.
Engage the class in a Convince Me! discussion as explained on
pages T6 to T12.

- $\begin{array}{r} 22 \\ + 24 \end{array}$ **(46)**

- $\begin{array}{r} 95 \\ + 85 \end{array}$ **(180)**

- $120 - 15 = $ **(105)**

- $\begin{array}{r} 110 \\ - 107 \end{array}$ **(3)**

- $\begin{array}{r} 77 \\ - 50 \end{array}$ **(27)**

- $\begin{array}{r} 5 \\ \times \quad 9 \end{array}$ **(45)**

- $\begin{array}{r} 5 \\ \times \quad 6 \end{array}$ **(30)**

- $64 \div 8 = $ **(8)**

Topic: Discussions   **Focus:** Computation strategies

MathLand®: Grade Four
© Creative Publications

Measure Up

Let's talk about measurement. Put the transparent ruler on the overhead projector. Say, *If there are 12 inches in 1 foot, how many inches are there in 2 feet? Let's say the answer together.* Then ask, *How many inches in 3 feet?*

Try, *If 1 foot is the same as 12 inches, how many feet are there in 24 inches?* Try other similar conversions between feet and inches.

Topic: Measurement   **Focus:** Converting inches to feet

Convince Me!

Ask the following questions. Engage the class in a Convince Me! discussion as explained on pages T6 to T12.

- *There are 60 seconds in 1 minute. How many seconds are there in 5 minutes?* (300 seconds)

- *There are 60 minutes in 1 hour. How many minutes are there in 6 hours?* (360 minutes)

- *There are 24 hours in 1 day. How many hours are there in 5 days?* (120 hours)

Draw Me!

It's a Miniboard day again! You're going to draw some fractions on your boards. Draw a circle on your boards. Now shade in $\frac{1}{2}$ of it. Name the following shapes and fractional parts one at a time, and give the students time to draw them. On your signal, the students should show their Miniboards.

Try these:

• **Draw a square; shade in $\frac{1}{4}$ of it.**

• **Draw a rectangle; shade in $\frac{1}{3}$ of it.**

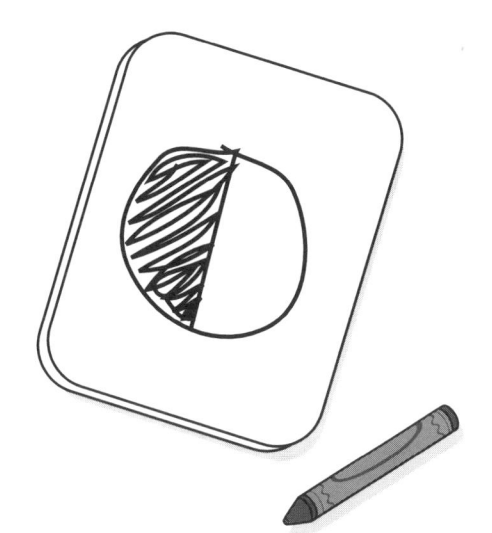

Topic: Fractions   **Focus:** Representing by a drawing

Write the following problems on the chalkboard one at a time.
Engage the class in a Convince Me! discussion as explained on
pages T6 to T12.

- 101
  + 67 **(168)**

-   14
  ×   4 **(56)**

- 36 ÷ 6 = **(6)**

- 200
  − 55 **(145)**

-   200
  + 84 **(284)**

- 3 × 12 = **(36)**

- 49 ÷ 7 = **(7)**

-   300
  − 124 **(176)**

Topic: Discussions   **Focus:** Computation strategies

They're Connected!

Let's do more math in our heads. Listen closely, then we'll all say the answer together. Ready? 5 × 3. Wait a second, then say the answer with the students and continue: *5 × 30, 5 × 300.*

Fifteen!

Try these:

- *4 × 7, 4 × 70, 4 × 700*
- *8 × 9, 8 × 90, 8 × 900*

Topic: Mental arithmetic **Focus:** Related multiplication MathLand® : Grade Four

53 Convince Me!

Write on the chalkboard: 2 + 3 = _____; 20 + 30 = _____; 200 + 300 = _____; 2000 + 3000 = _____. Ask the students, *If 2 + 3 = 5, what's 20 + 30? What's 200 + 300? What's 2000 + 3000?* Engage the class in a Convince Me! discussion as explained on pages T6 to T12.

$$2+3=5$$

Times Tables

Do you know your multiplication facts for 7? Let's say them all together for practice: 7 × 0 is 0, 7 × 1 is 7, 7 × 2 is 14,.... Start with the students, then let them go ahead on their own.

Repeat with the times tables for other multiplication facts.

55   **Convince Me!**

Write the following problems on the chalkboard one at a time.
Engage the class in a Convince Me! discussion as explained on
pages T6 to T12.

- $0.75 + $0.55 = **($1.30)**

- $0.85
  +   0.35   **($1.20)**

- $1.25
  −   0.75   **($0.50)**

- $2.50
  −   0.85   **($1.65)**

- $0.89
  +   0.75   **($1.64)**

- $0.97
  +   0.68   **($1.65)**

- $1.50
  −   0.65   **($0.85)**

- $2.00 − $1.75 = **($0.25)**

Topic: Discussions   **Focus:** Computation strategies, money

Today we're going to do money math in our heads. Listen closely. I'll give you a minute to think and then we'll all say the answer together. Ready? Begin: $0.25 × 2.

Try these:

- *$0.15 × 3* ($0.45)
- *$0.30 × 3* ($0.90)
- *$0.40 × 6* ($2.40)
- *$0.20 × 5* ($1.00)

Fifty cents!

Name That Number

Let's name some large numbers. I'll write some here on the overhead projector and you say their names with me. Ready? Write the following numbers one at a time, naming each number with the students after you write it.

Twenty thousand, four hundred, and eleven

Try these:

- 20,411; 36,318; 19,062

- 38,194; 41,278; 44,360

- 200,000; 149,122; 108,180

Convince Me!

Write the following problems on the chalkboard one at a time.
Engage the class in a Convince Me! discussion as explained on
pages T6 to T12.

- $\begin{array}{r} 38 \\ + \ 18 \end{array}$ **(56)**

- $\begin{array}{r} 65 \\ + \ 16 \end{array}$ **(81)**

- $12 \times 5 =$ **(60)**

- $56 \div 7 =$ **(8)**

- $\begin{array}{r} 150 \\ - \ 99 \end{array}$ **(51)**

- $\begin{array}{r} 140 \\ - \ 77 \end{array}$ **(63)**

- $\begin{array}{r} 106 \\ + \ 345 \end{array}$ **(451)**

- $\begin{array}{r} 112 \\ + \ 249 \end{array}$ **(361)**

Topic: Discussions   **Focus:** Computation strategies

What Number Is Missing?

Time for pattern practice! I'll write a number pattern and you figure out the number that is missing. Write a number pattern on the overhead projector, leaving a space where one number is missing. Pause for two or three seconds and then have the students say the pattern, including the missing number.

102, 104, 106, 108 . . .

Try these:

• 102, 104, ___, 108, 110 **(106)**

• 310, ___, 330, 340 **(320)**

• 555, 560, 565, ___, 575 **(570)**

1. [Write: 112, 114, _____ , 118, 120] *Write the missing number.*   116
2. *Write the number I say: forty-one thousand, fifty-two.*   41,052
3. [Write: 6325 _____ 6352] *Use the greater than or less than sign to make this statement true.* $<$
4. *Draw a rectangle and shade $\frac{1}{4}$ of it.*   vary
5. [Write: 6 × 400] *Write the answer to this problem.*   2400
6. [Write: 6437 − 5328] *Name two numbers the answer falls between.*   vary
7. [Write: $0.40 × 5] *Write the answer to this problem.* $2.00
8. *How many inches are there in 3 feet?*   36 inches
9. [Write: 500, _____ , 1500, 2000, _____] *Write the missing numbers.*   1000, 2500
10. *How many minutes are in $1\frac{1}{2}$ hours.*   90

61 Convince Me!

Read this story problem to the class. *There are 12 girls getting ready for a hike. They are making sandwiches. Each girl plans to eat 3 sandwiches. How many sandwiches do they need to make in all?* Engage the class in a Convince Me! discussion as explained on pages T6 to T12. **(36)**

Topic: Discussions   **Focus:** Computation strategies

You Draw It!

Today you're going to sketch Base Ten Blocks on your Miniboards. Are you ready? Write the number 137 on the overhead projector. ***Look at this number. Now sketch the Base Ten Blocks that would show this number. Write the number beside them.*** On your signal, the students should show their Miniboards. Continue, having the students sketch other block combinations.

Try these:

• 116

• 240

• 201

• 129

Convince Me!

Write the following problems on the chalkboard one at a time. Engage the class in a Convince Me! discussion as explained on pages T6 to T12.

- $\begin{array}{r} 100 \\ + 130 \\ \hline \end{array}$ **(230)**

- $\begin{array}{r} 200 \\ + 60 \\ \hline \end{array}$ **(260)**

- $\begin{array}{r} 850 \\ - 25 \\ \hline \end{array}$ **(825)**

- $32 \div 4 = $ **(8)**

- $5 \times 6 = $ **(30)**

- $\begin{array}{r} 650 \\ - 75 \\ \hline \end{array}$ **(575)**

- $\begin{array}{r} 528 \\ - 505 \\ \hline \end{array}$ **(23)**

- $\begin{array}{r} 238 \\ - 168 \\ \hline \end{array}$ **(70)**

Topic: Discussions **Focus:** Computation strategies

What Comes Between?

Get your Miniboards ready! I'm going to write two numbers on the overhead projector. I'd like for you to write the number that comes in between them. On your signal, the class should show their Miniboards and say the number.

Try these:

- 1224, 1226 **(1225)**

- 3412, 3414 **(3413)**

- 5678, 5680 **(5679)**

- 7539, 7541 **(7540)**

Topic: Sequencing numbers, greater than 1000   **Focus:** Numbers between two numbers

65 ◆ Convince Me!

Read this story problem to the class. ***If 13 cats each had 7 kittens, how many kittens are there in all?*** Engage the class in a Convince Me! discussion as explained on pages T6 to T12. **(91)**

Convince Me!

Write the following problems on the chalkboard one at a time.
Engage the class in a Convince Me! discussion as explained on
pages T6 to T12.

- $\begin{array}{r} 123 \\ +\ \ 25 \end{array}$ (148)

- $\begin{array}{r} 176 \\ +\ \ 28 \end{array}$ (204)

- $\begin{array}{r} 539 \\ -\ \ 28 \end{array}$ (511)

- $\begin{array}{r} 493 \\ -\ \ 72 \end{array}$ (421)

- $9 \times 8 = $ (72)

- $\begin{array}{r} 217 \\ +\ 379 \end{array}$ (596)

- $\begin{array}{r} 215 \\ +\ 375 \end{array}$ (590)

- $100 \div 4 = $ (25)

Convince Me!

Write on the chalkboard: 7 + 6 = ____; 70 + 60 = ____;
700 + 600 = ____; 7000 + 6000 = ____. Ask the students,
*If 7 + 6 = 13, what's 70 + 60? What's 700 + 600?
What's 7000 + 6000?* Engage the class in a Convince Me!
discussion as explained on pages T6 to T12.

Convince Me!

Write the following problems on the chalkboard one at a time.
Engage the class in a Convince Me! discussion as explained on
pages T6 to T12.

- $\begin{array}{r} 51 \\ + 19 \\ \hline \end{array}$ (70)

- $\begin{array}{r} 62 \\ + 18 \\ \hline \end{array}$ (80)

- $\begin{array}{r} 75 \\ - 68 \\ \hline \end{array}$ (7)

- $\begin{array}{r} 86 \\ - 59 \\ \hline \end{array}$ (27)

- $\begin{array}{r} 25 \\ \times \ 5 \\ \hline \end{array}$ (125)

- $63 \div 9 = $ (7)

- $45 \div 5 = $ (9)

- $\begin{array}{r} 14 \\ \times \ 3 \\ \hline \end{array}$ (42)

Topic: Discussions   **Focus:** Computation strategies   MathLand®: Grade Four
© Creative Publications

It's Miniboard time! Let's look at the Fraction Circles again.
Use transparent Fraction Circles on the overhead projector to
show different fractions. Ask the students to write numerals to
name the fractions you show, one at a time. On your signal, the
students should show their Miniboards.

Try these:

- $\frac{1}{2}$ • $\frac{2}{4}$

- $\frac{1}{5}$ • $\frac{3}{4}$

- $\frac{2}{3}$ • $\frac{4}{5}$

Topic: Fractions   **Focus:** Writing names

MathLand®: Grade Four
© Creative Publications

70 ◆ **Convince Me!**

Ask the following questions. Engage the class in a Convince Me! discussion as explained on pages T6 to T12.

- *There are 60 minutes in 1 hour. How many minutes are there in 2 hours?* (120 minutes)

- *There are 24 hours in a day. How many hours are there in 2 days?* (48 hours)

Measure Up

Let's talk about measurement. Put a transparent centimeter ruler on the overhead projector. Draw a line that is exactly 10 centimeters long. Read the line length with the students, ***It's 10 centimeters.*** Mark off other lines in centimeter lengths and have the class say the lengths. Each time they name a length, write it by the line.

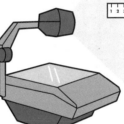

Convince Me!

Write the following problems on the chalkboard one at a time. Engage the class in a Convince Me! discussion as explained on pages T6 to T12.

- $1.75
  + 1.25   ($3.00)

- $2.00
  + 1.81   ($3.81)

- $0.75
  + 1.50   ($2.25)

- $2.50
  + 1.75   ($4.25)

- $2.00
  × 3   ($6.00)

- $5.00 ÷ 4 = ($1.25)

- $1.50 × 4 = ($6.00)

- $3.25
  × 4   ($13.00)

$1.75
+ 1.25

Listen and Think

Today we're going to do some more money math in our heads.
Listen closely. I'll give you a minute to think and then we'll
all say the answer together. Ready? Begin: $2.50 × 2.

Five Dollars!

Try these:

- *$5.00 × 3* ($15.00)

- *$3.00 × 4* ($12.00)

- *$6.50 × 3* ($19.50)

- *$5.25 × 4* ($21.00)

Topic: Mental arithmetic

Focus: Computation, money

Time to get your Miniboards out! Let's do more math thinking.
Put 20 Rainbow Cubes on the overhead projector with the light
off. *Some alligators are marching to the river to swim.* Group
the cubes in twos. *There are 10 pairs of 2 alligators starting to
march. How many alligators are marching to the river? When
you know the answer, write it on your Miniboard.* Turn on the
light to show the correct answer. On your signal, the class should
show their Miniboards.

Repeat, using different numbers of cubes.

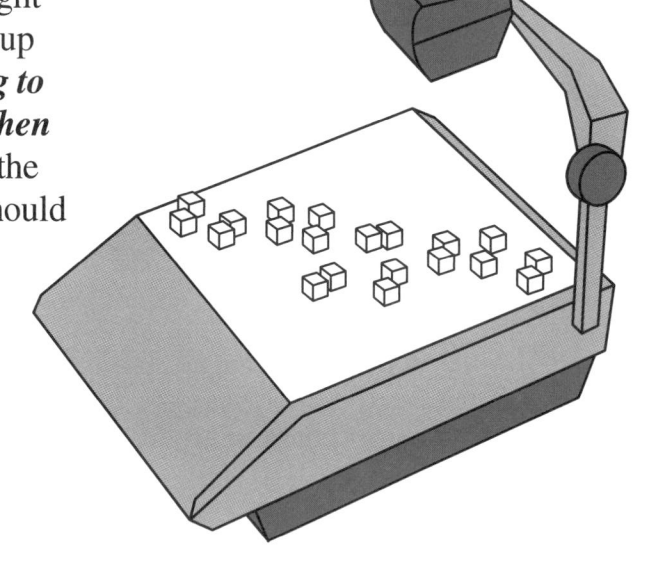

Topic: Mental arithmetic   **Focus:** Visualizing multiplication

MathLand®: Grade Four
© Creative Publications

Convince Me!

Read this story problem to the class. *I saw 14 boys fishing from a pier. They each had 6 worms to put on their hooks. How many worms were there in all?* Engage the class in a Convince Me! discussion as explained on pages T6 to T12. (**84 worms**)

Convince Me!

Write the following problems on the chalkboard one at a time.
Engage the class in a Convince Me! discussion as explained on
pages T6 to T12.

- $\begin{array}{r} 759 \\ + \ 500 \end{array}$ **(1259)**

- $14 \times 5 =$ **(70)**

- $64 \div 8 =$ **(8)**

- $\begin{array}{r} 408 \\ - \ 375 \end{array}$ **(33)**

- $\begin{array}{r} 800 \\ + \ 400 \end{array}$ **(1200)**

- $\begin{array}{r} 12 \\ \times \quad 6 \end{array}$ **(72)**

- $\begin{array}{r} 328 \\ - \ 149 \end{array}$ **(179)**

- $81 \div 9 =$ **(9)**

It's a Miniboard day! Look up here at the overhead projector. I'll write some money problems on it. You copy them on your Miniboards and then write the answers. Write: $0.15 × 4 = ____; $0.50 × 3 = ____; $0.40 × 5 = ____. Give the students time to write, then have them show their Miniboards. (**$0.60; $1.50; $2.00**)

Repeat with the following equations: $0.75 × 3 = ____; $1.00 × 5 = ____; $2.50 × 4 = ____. (**$2.25; $5.00; $10.00**)

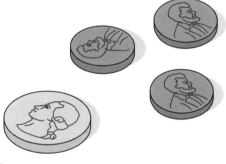

Topic: Number facts   **Focus:** Money problems

MathLand®: Grade Four
© Creative Publications

Draw on the chalkboard a line that is 1 meter long. Mark off a few centimeters on the line. Ask the following questions. Engage the class in a Convince Me! discussion as explained on pages T6 to T12.

- *There are 100 centimeters in 1 meter. How many centimeters are there in 2 meters?* (200 cm)

- *How many centimeters are there in one-half a meter?* (50 cm)

- *How many meters do you have if there are 300 centimeters?* (3 m)

Write It Down!

Let's practice writing numbers on paper. I'll say some numbers and you write them as neatly as you can on your paper. Afterwards we'll read them all together. Are you ready? Say the following numbers slowly giving the students time to write them. After the students have finished, read the numbers aloud with them.

Try these:

- 10,000; 14,209; 16,327

- 17,338; 32,391; 26,867

- 11,002; 50,823; 61,564

Topic: Number recognition, greater than 10,000   **Focus:** Writing numbers

Answers

1. [Write: 90, 87, 84, 81, ____] *Write the number that comes next.* — 78
2. [Rainbow Cubes: a row of 8 and a row of 9] *Is there an even or odd number of cubes?* — odd
3. *Write the number I say: seventy-two thousand, six hundred seventy-five.* — 72,675
4. [Write: 5622, ____ , 5624] *Write the number that comes between.* — 5623
5. [Fraction Circles: 2 fifth pieces] *Write the fraction.* — $\frac{2}{5}$
6. *I have nine pairs of shoes in my closet. How many shoes do I have?* — 18
7. *What is the number of centimeters in a meter?* — 100
8. [Write: $0.75 × 5] *Write the answer.* — $3.75
9. [Centimeter ruler. Draw a 20 centimeter line.] *Write the length of this line.* — 20 cm
10. [Base Ten Blocks: 1 hundred, 4 tens, 6 ones] *Write this number.* — 146

Convince Me!

Write the following problems on the chalkboard one at a time. Engage the class in a Convince Me! discussion as explained on pages T6 to T12.

- 146
  − 103   **(43)**

- 9 × 10 = **(90)**

- 87
  + 413   **(500)**

- 25
  ×   6   **(150)**

- 222
  − 140   **(82)**

- 743
  +   57   **(800)**

- 20
  ×   9   **(180)**

- 75 ÷ 25 = **(3)**

Topic: Discussions   **Focus:** Computation strategies

Miniboards out! Are you ready? With the light off, put 2 rows of 4 transparent Base Ten ones blocks on the overhead projector. Say, *I put 2 rows of 4 blocks each up here. Draw a picture of what they look like; write the multiplication equation they show, and the answer.* After the students have finished, turn on the light so they can see the blocks. On your signal, the class should show their Miniboards.

Try these:

- 3 rows with 6 in each row $(3 \times 6 = 18)$

- 2 rows with 12 in each row $(2 \times 12 = 24)$

- 3 rows with 9 in each row $(3 \times 9 = 27)$

Read this story problem to the class. ***Jerry has 50 tropical fish in a tank. Merry has 38 fish in her tank. How many more fish does Merry need, to have as many as Jerry?*** Engage the class in a Convince Me! discussion as explained on pages T6 to T12. **(12)**

On the Nose!

I'm thinking of a number between 1 and 10,000. I'll write it here. With the overhead projector light off, write the number on the projector. *Can you guess it?* Call on individual students to try to guess the number. After each guess say, *higher* or *lower*. Continue until the correct number is guessed. Then turn the projector light on to reveal the number and say, *On the nose!*

85 ▷ Convince Me!

Write the following problems on the chalkboard one at a time.
Engage the class in a Convince Me! discussion as explained on
pages T6 to T12.

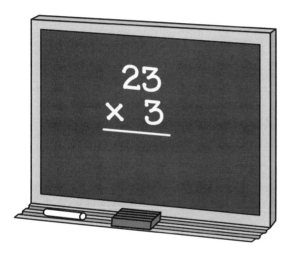

- $\begin{array}{r} 23 \\ \times\ 3 \end{array}$ **(69)**

- $\begin{array}{r} 16 \\ \times\ 4 \end{array}$ **(64)**

- $48 + 413 =$ **(461)**

- $\begin{array}{r} 747 \\ \times\ 28 \end{array}$ **(20,916)**

- $\begin{array}{r} 646 \\ -\ 106 \end{array}$ **(540)**

- $35 \div 7 =$ **(5)**

- $24 \div 8 =$ **(3)**

- $\begin{array}{r} 986 \\ -\ 872 \end{array}$ **(114)**

Convince Me!

Read this story problem to the class. *If there are 60 jellybeans in a bag, how many little cups holding 5 beans each can you fill with them?* Engage the class in a Convince Me! discussion as explained on pages T6 to T12. (**12**)

Imagine This!

Miniboards out! We're going to do some more work with fractions. With the light off, draw a circle on the overhead projector. Say, *I've drawn a circle. Imagine what it looks like. Now I'm dividing it into 4 equal parts. I'm shading in 1 part. You draw the same picture on your Miniboards and then write the fraction name of the shaded part.*

After the students have had time to make their drawings, turn on the light to reveal your drawing. At your signal, the students should hold up their Miniboards. Repeat with other fractions.

For a challenge, have the students write the fraction name of the unshaded part of the circle.

Topic: Fractions **Focus:** Recognizing from a description

What's Half?

We're going to talk about parts of numbers. I'll put some cubes up here on the overhead projector and you listen for my question. Put 12 Rainbow Cubes on the overhead and ask, *What's $\frac{1}{2}$ of 12?* After the students have replied, divide the cubes into 2 groups of 6. Continue with other fraction questions, each time showing the cubes on the overhead.

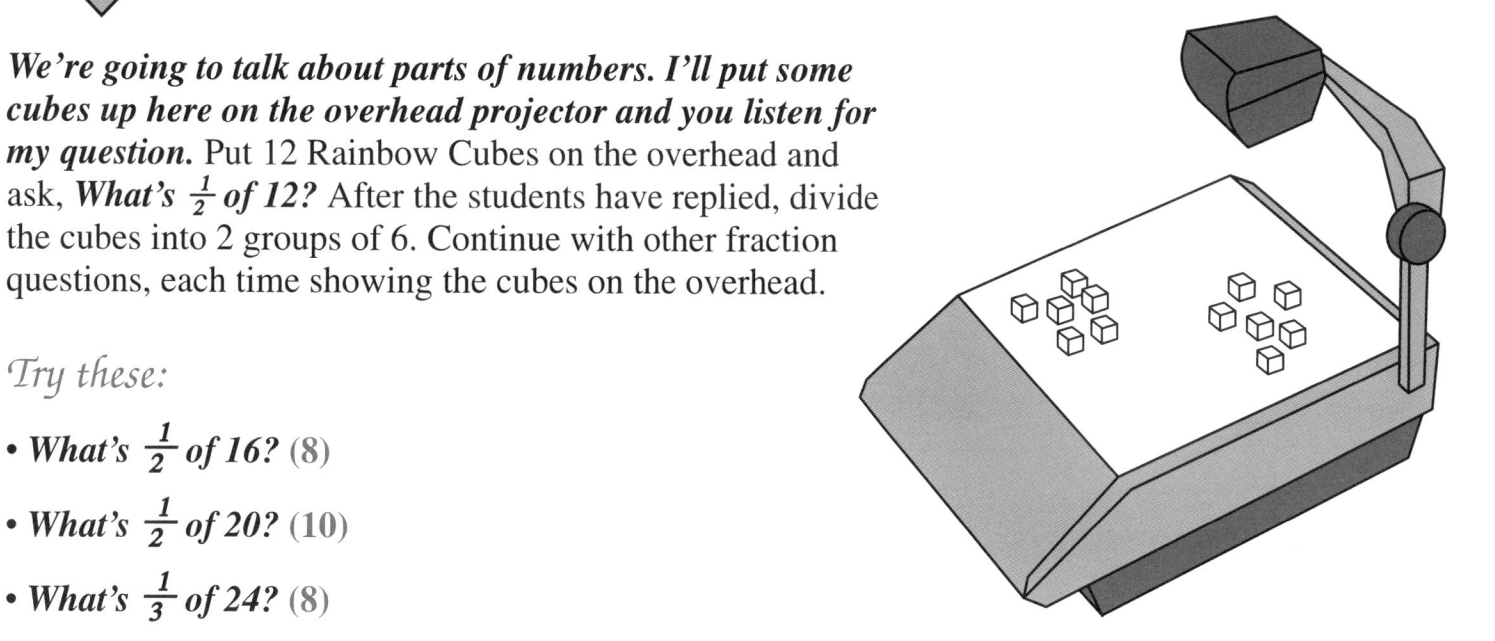

Try these:

• *What's $\frac{1}{2}$ of 16?* (8)

• *What's $\frac{1}{2}$ of 20?* (10)

• *What's $\frac{1}{3}$ of 24?* (8)

Topic: Fractions   **Focus:** Finding fractional parts

89   Convince Me!

Write the following problems on the chalkboard one at a time. Engage the class in a Convince Me! discussion as explained on pages T6 to T12.

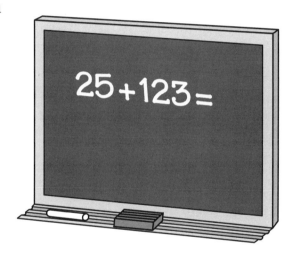

- 25 + 123 = **(148)**

- 322
  − 244   **(78)**

- 23
  ×   4   **(92)**

- 285
  + 672   **(957)**

- 284
  +   37   **(321)**

- 526
  − 315   **(211)**

- 15
  ×   4   **(60)**

- 75 ÷ 15 = **(5)**

Topic: Discussions   **Focus:** Computation strategies

Measure Up

Time for more measurement! Put a transparent inch ruler on the overhead projector. Draw a line that is exactly $2\frac{1}{2}$ inches long. Ask the students to read the ruler and tell how long the line is. Mark off other lines in half-inch lengths and have the class tell the lengths. Each time they name a length, write it by the line.

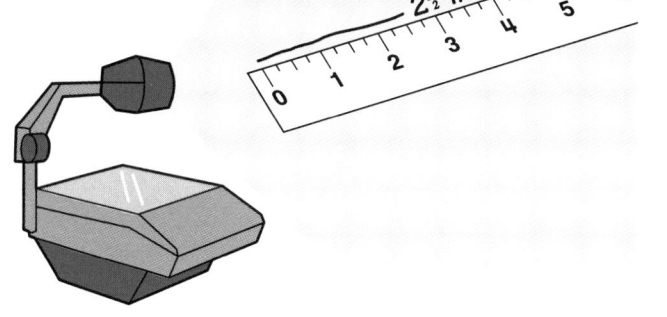

Convince Me!

Ask the following questions, one at a time. Engage the class in a Convince Me! discussion as explained on pages T6 to T12.

- *I have 20 counters and $\frac{1}{2}$ of them are green. How many counters are green?* (10)

- *I have 20 counters and $\frac{1}{4}$ of them are red. How many are red?* (5)

- *I have 15 counters and $\frac{1}{3}$ of them are yellow. How many are yellow?* (5)

What's It Between?

Today we're going to do some estimating again. I'll write a multiplication problem here on the overhead projector and give you a few seconds to look at it. Then I'll ask someone to tell us two numbers that the answer is between. Ready? Write 147 × 9 on the overhead, turn on the light for about 3 seconds, then turn it off. ***Let's name two numbers that the answer would fall between.*** See if anyone wants to narrow the range. Ask the students why they came up with those numbers.
(exact answer = 1323)

Try these:

- 236
  × 3
  (708)

- 172
  × 5
  (860)

(Exact answers are shown.)

Topic: Estimation　　　　　　**Focus:** Finding a range of numbers

93 ◇ Convince Me!

Write the following problems on the chalkboard one at a time. Engage the class in a Convince Me! discussion as explained on pages T6 to T12.

- $0.25
  × 3   ($0.75)

- $0.60
  × 2   ($1.20)

- $0.55
  × 4   ($2.20)

- $1.50
  × 5   ($7.50)

- $1.50 × 8 = ($12.00)

- $1.25
  × 8   ($10.00)

- $0.50
  × 5   ($2.50)

- $0.75 × 3 = ($2.25)

Billions and Millions

Prepare four index cards for this activity. On one write Billion; on one write Million; on one write Thousand, and leave the last one blank. Set the cards up in that order, left to right, in the chalktray. Above the Billion card, write 821. Above the Million card, write 146. Above the Thousand card, write 379, and above the blank card, write 258.

Today you're going to read a number in the billions. Read with the students: *Eight hundred twenty-one billion, one hundred forty-six million, three hundred seventy-nine thousand, two hundred fifty-eight.* Let various students take turns saying the number by themselves. Then have the students practice saying the number, but this time turn the cards over so the blank sides face the class.

Repeat, writing other three-digit numbers above the cards.

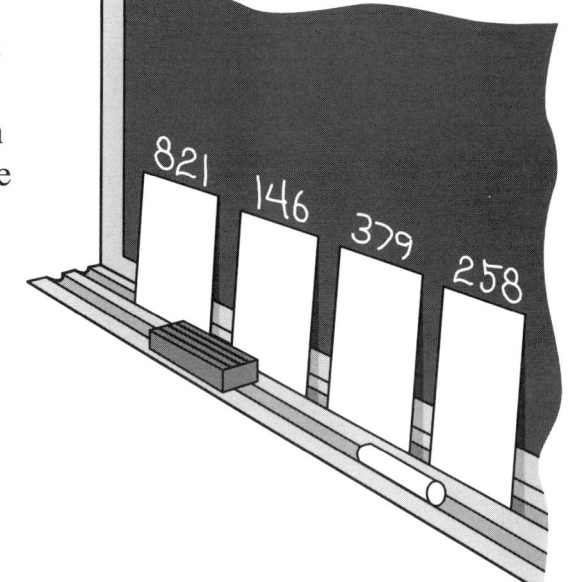

Topic: Place value   **Focus:** Learning period names

95 How Much Time?

Today we're going to talk about time. It's time for your Miniboards, too. Watch what I write up here on the overhead projector and then write the answer to my question. Write: 60 seconds = 1 minute. Ask, *How many seconds are there in 2 minutes? Write the answer.* On your signal, the class should show their Miniboards.

Try these:

- Write: 60 minutes = 1 hour. *How many minutes are there in 3 hours? How many minutes are there in 4 hours?* (180; 240)

- Write: 24 hours = 1 day. *How many hours are there in 4 days?* (96)

What's Half?

Today is a Miniboard day! We're going to talk about parts of numbers. I'll put some cubes up here on the overhead projector. You listen to my question, then write the answer on your Miniboard. Put 24 Rainbow Cubes on the overhead and ask, ***What's*** $\frac{1}{2}$ ***of 24?*** After students have written their numbers, divide the cubes into 2 groups of 12. Continue with other fraction questions, each time showing the cubes on the overhead. On your signal, the class should show their Miniboards.

Try these:

- *What's* $\frac{1}{2}$ *of 18?* (9)

- *What's* $\frac{1}{4}$ *of 8?* (2)

- *What's* $\frac{1}{3}$ *of 12?* (4)

Topic: Fractions   **Focus:** Finding fractional parts

Imagine This!

It's Miniboard time again! We're going to work some more with fractions. With the light off, draw a rectangle on the overhead projector. Say, *I've drawn a rectangle. Imagine what it looks like. Now I'm dividing it into 5 equal parts. I'm shading in 3 parts. You draw the same picture on your Miniboards and then write the fraction name of the shaded part.*

After the students have had time to make their drawings, turn on the light to reveal your drawing. At your signal, the students should hold up their Miniboards. Repeat with other fractions.

For a challenge, have the students write the fraction name of the unshaded part of the rectangle.

Topic: Fractions   **Focus:** Recognizing from a description

Convince Me!

Read this story problem to the class. ***The animal shelter has 77 cats and 98 dogs. How many more dogs than cats are at the shelter?*** Engage the class in a Convince Me! discussion as explained on pages T6 to T12. **(21)**

It's a Miniboard day! You're going to write money amounts in dollars and cents. I'll say amounts of money, you'll write them on your Miniboards. Ready? Here goes! Say the following amounts and give the students time to write them. On your signal, the students should show their Miniboards.

Try these:

- $0.75, $0.39, $0.12

- $1.25, $1.53, $9.18

- $5.16, $7.08, $47.89

Answers

1. [Write: 47,932; 76,423; 76,324] *Write the largest number.* — 76,423
2. *What is $\frac{1}{4}$ of 12?* — 3
3. *How many wheels on 5 bicycles?* — 10
4. [Write: 136 × 8] *Name two numbers the answer falls between.* — vary
5. *Write the money amount I say in dollars and cents: $57.32.* — $57.32
6. *How many minutes are there in five hours?* — 300
7. [3 rows of 5 blocks] *Write the multiplication equation the blocks show.* — $3 \times 5 = 15$
8. [Inch Ruler: Draw $3\frac{1}{2}$ inch line.] *How long is this line?* — $3\frac{1}{2}$ inches
9. [Polygon Tiles: triangle, parallelogram] *Draw the shape that is a parallelogram.* — sketch
10. *Write the number I say: three hundred twenty-one million.* — 321,000,000

Convince Me!

Write the following problems on the chalkboard one at a time.
Engage the class in a Convince Me! discussion as explained on
pages T6 to T12.

- $$\begin{array}{r} 175 \\ + 155 \\ \hline \end{array}$$ **(330)**

- $$\begin{array}{r} 263 \\ + 451 \\ \hline \end{array}$$ **(714)**

- $$\begin{array}{r} 425 \\ - 170 \\ \hline \end{array}$$ **(255)**

- $$\begin{array}{r} 600 \\ - 480 \\ \hline \end{array}$$ **(120)**

- $$\begin{array}{r} 24 \\ \times \ 10 \\ \hline \end{array}$$ **(240)**

- $80 \div 4 =$ **(20)**

- $60 \div 2 =$ **(30)**

- $$\begin{array}{r} 12 \\ \times \ 12 \\ \hline \end{array}$$ **(144)**

Topic: Discussions **Focus:** Computation strategies

How Much?

*Let's play the **How Much?** game. Listen very closely because you are going to have to add and take away amounts of money in your heads.* Name the following coins slowly and have the class say the final value.

Try these:

- *quarter, dime, take away penny, take away penny* ($0.33)

- *quarter, quarter, dime, nickel, nickel* ($0.70)

- *quarter, nickel, take away dime, penny* ($0.21)

- *half dollar, quarter, dime, take away nickel* ($0.80)

Convince Me!

Write on the chalkboard: 15 + 15 = ____;
150 + 150 = ____; 1500 + 1500 = ____.
Ask the students, *If 15 + 15 = 30, what's
150 + 150? What's 1500 + 1500?* Engage
the class in a Convince Me! discussion as
explained on pages T6 to T12.

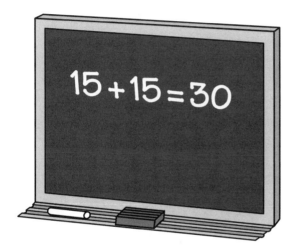

Hidden Blocks

It's a Miniboard day! Put these transparent Base Ten Blocks on the overhead projector: 6 tens blocks and 5 ones blocks. Cover 2 tens blocks and 2 ones blocks with a card. Turn on the light and say, *These blocks show 65 in all.* Write 65 on the overhead. *However, I've covered some of them. Make a drawing on your Miniboards of the covered blocks.* Wait until most of the students are finished, then ask one student to name the hidden blocks.

Try the activity again, this time covering different blocks.

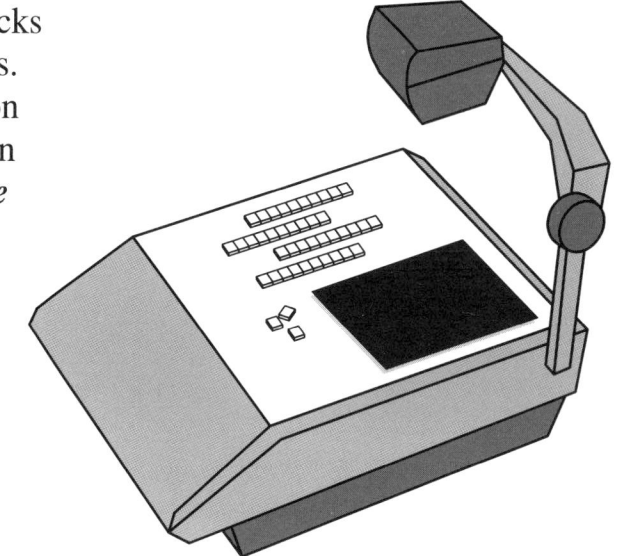

How Many Halves?

We're going to talk about fractions today. I'll draw some fractions on the overhead projector and ask a question. Ready?
Draw 2 squares and $\frac{1}{2}$ a square on the overhead. Ask, *How many halves is $2\frac{1}{2}$?* Say with the students, *Five halves.*
Continue with other fraction questions, each time drawing squares and parts of squares on the overhead.

Try these:

• *How many halves is 1 whole?* (2)

• *How many halves is $3\frac{1}{2}$?* (7)

• *How many halves is 4?* (8)

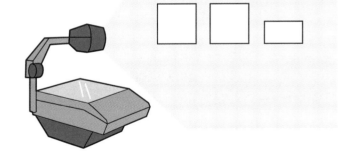

Topic: Fractions

Focus: Naming mixed numbers

MathLand®: Grade Four
© Creative Publications

Ask the following questions. Engage the class in a Convince Me! discussion as explained on pages T6 to T12.

- *There are 7 days in 1 week. How many days are there in 3 weeks?* (21 days)

- *There are 30 days in some months. How many days are there in 4 of those months?* (120 days)

- *There are 365 days in most years. How many days are there in 2 years?* (730 days)

S	M	T	W	T	F	S
				1	2	3
4	5	6	7	8	9	10
11	12	13	14	15	16	17
18	19	20	21	22	23	24
25	26	27	28	29	30	

Greater Than, Less Than

It's a Miniboard day again! We're going to think about numbers that are "greater than" or "less than" other numbers. I'll say, "greater than 5182" and you write any number that comes after 5182. I'll say, "less than 1000" and you write any number that comes before 1000. After writing each number, the students should show their Miniboards.

Try these:

- **Greater than 7329**

- **Less than 1943**

- **Greater than 6091**

- **Less than 10,000**

Ask the following question and let several students give answers. ***How many thirds is $1\frac{2}{3}$?*** Engage the class in a Convince Me! discussion as explained on pages T6 to T12.

$$(1\frac{2}{3} = \frac{5}{3})$$

Time for Miniboards again! You're going to write two names for one fraction. Use transparent and opaque Fraction Circles on the overhead projector to show the fraction. Put on one whole region, covered by 2 halves, and another opaque $\frac{1}{2}$ piece beside it. Turn on the light and say, ***Write two different names for this fraction.*** After giving students time to write, ask, ***Who can tell one name for this fraction? Who knows another name for the same fraction?*** On your signal, the students should show their Miniboards.

Try these:

- $\frac{3}{3}$ **(1)**
- $\frac{8}{5}$ $\left(\mathbf{1\frac{3}{5}}\right)$
- $\frac{7}{4}$ $\left(\mathbf{1\frac{3}{4}}\right)$
- $\frac{4}{2}$ **(2)**

Topic: Fractions   **Focus:** Naming mixed numbers

Let's talk about measurement. Put an inch ruler on the overhead. Say, ***There are 12 inches in 1 foot. How many inches are there in 3 feet? Let's say the answer together.*** (36 inches) Then ask, ***How many inches in 6 feet?*** (72 inches)

Try, ***If 1 foot is the same as 12 inches, how many feet are in 48 inches?*** (4 feet)

Try other similar conversions between inches and feet.

Convince Me!

Write the following problems on the chalkboard one at a time. Engage the class in a Convince Me! discussion as explained on pages T6 to T12.

- 220
  − 30   **(190)**

- 1764
  + 312   **(2076)**

- 3375
  + 182   **(3557)**

- 1234
  − 417   **(817)**

- 13 × 3 = **(39)**

- 17
  × 2   **(34)**

- 205
  − 75   **(130)**

- 90 ÷ 10 = **(9)**

Topic: Discussions   **Focus:** Computation strategies

What's It Between?

Time for some estimating with division! I'll write a division problem here on the overhead projector and give you a few seconds to look at it. Then I'll ask you to say two numbers the answer is between. Ready? Write 1500 ÷ 510 = ____ on the overhead, turn on the light for about 3 seconds, then turn it off. *Let's name two numbers that the answer would fall between.* See if anyone wants to narrow the range. Ask the students why they came up with those numbers. (**actual answer** = **2.94 or 2R480**)

1500÷510=

Convince Me!

Ask the following question and let several students give answers. ***How much is 7 halves?*** Engage the class in a Convince Me! discussion as explained on pages T6 to T12.

$$\left(\frac{7}{2} = 3\frac{1}{2}\right)$$

How Long?

It's Miniboard and measurement time again! Put a transparent centimeter ruler on the overhead projector. Draw a line that is exactly 5 centimeters long. Ask the students to write on their Miniboards how long the line is. Mark off other lines in centimeter lengths and have the students write those lengths. On your signal, have the students show their Miniboards.

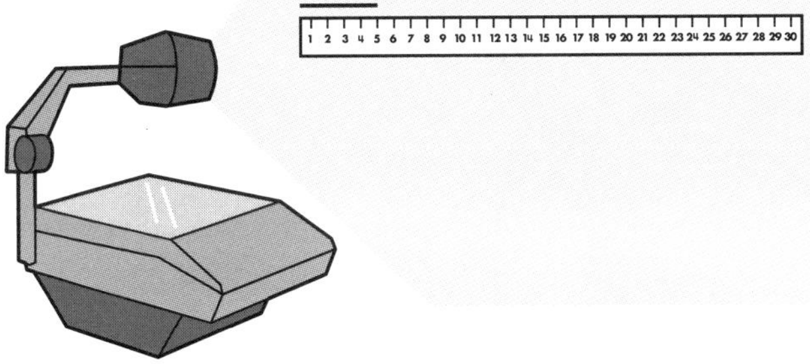

Try these:

- 4 centimeters

- 7 centimeters

- 8 centimeters

Convince Me!

Read this story problem to the class. *If there are 48 eggs in a basket, how many cartons holding 12 eggs each can you fill with them?* Engage the class in a Convince Me! discussion as explained on pages T6 to T12. **(4 cartons)**

How Much Is Hidden?

Let's play a coin game. I'll put some coins on the overhead projector and tell you their total value. Then I'll cover some of them with my hand and you tell me what coins I could be hiding. Put transparent coins, 3 dimes, 1 nickel, and 1 penny on the overhead with the light off. Say, ***These coins are worth 36¢.*** Cover 1 dime and the penny. Turn the light on and ask the students to say what coins you could be hiding.

After the students have guessed correctly, hide a different set of coins.

Missing Signs

Let's do more missing signs problems. Get your Miniboards ready! I'm going to write an equation on the overhead projector. But I'll put circles where the operations signs go. You write the equation on your Miniboards and put in signs to make the equation correct. Work inside the parentheses first. Here we go! Write the following equations one at a time, and give the class enough time to copy them and write the signs. Then read the complete equations together.

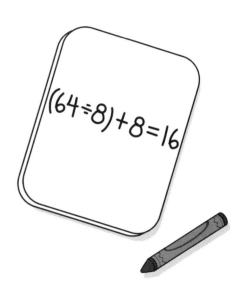

$(64 \div 8) + 8 = 16$

Try these:

- $(64 \bigcirc 8) \bigcirc 8 = 16$ $(\div, +)$
- $(12 \bigcirc 12) \bigcirc 8 = 8$ $(\div, \times)$
- $(2 \bigcirc 5) \bigcirc 3 = 13$ $(\times, +)$

Topic: Mental arithmetic

Focus: Computing mentally

Convince Me!

Write the following problems on the chalkboard one at a time.
Engage the class in a Convince Me! discussion as explained
on pages T6 to T12.

- $0.25
  × 6 **($1.50)**

- $0.75
  × 2 **($1.50)**

- $2.25 − $0.50 = **($1.75)**

- $1.25
  − 0.75 **($0.50)**

- $2.36
  + 0.81 **($3.17)**

- $0.75
  × 4 **($3.00)**

- $2.37
  + 0.37 **($2.74)**

- $5.00 ÷ 2 = **($2.50)**

$0.25×6=

119 Billions and Millions

Prepare four index cards for this activity. On one card write Billion; on one write Million; on one write Thousand, and leave the last one blank. Set the cards up in that order, left to right, in the chalktray. Above the Billion card, write 986. Above the Million card, write 754. Above the Thousand card, write 321, and above the blank card, write 480.

Today you're going to read a number in the billions. Read with the class: ***Nine hundred eighty-six billion, seven hundred fifty-four million, three hundred twenty-one thousand, four hundred eighty.*** Let various students take turns saying the number by themselves. Then have the students practice saying the number, but this time turn the cards over so the blank sides face the class.

Repeat, writing other three-digit numbers above the cards.

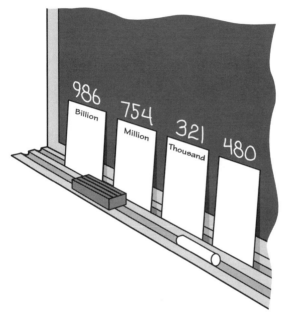

Topic: Place value   **Focus:** Learning period names

Answers

1. [Write: 10,340; _____ ; 10,400] *Write a number that comes between.*   vary

2. [Fraction Circles: Whole covered by 4 fourths, and 1 other $\frac{1}{4}$ piece] *Write two different names for this fraction.* $1\frac{1}{4}, \frac{5}{4}$

3. *Write the number I say: nine hundred forty-eight billion.*   948,000,000,000

4. [Write: 49 ◯ 7 ◯ 6 = 13] *Write the signs to make the equation correct.*   ÷ , +

5. [4 dimes, 2 nickels, 3 pennies: Cover 2 dimes, 2 pennies.] *I have 53¢ in all. What is the value of the covered coins?*   22¢

6. [Write: 1200 − 210] *Write two numbers the answer falls between.*   vary

7. *How many thirds in $2\frac{2}{3}$?*   8

8. *How many inches in 2 feet?*   24

9. [Polygon Tiles: trapezoid, rhombus] *Draw the rhombus.*   sketch

10. [Base Ten Blocks: 7 tens, 4 ones. Cover 3 tens and 2 ones. Write: 74] *Sketch the blocks that are covered.*   sketch of 32

121 Times Tables

Do you know your multiplication facts for nine? Let's say them all together for practice: 9 × 0 is 0, 9 × 1 is 9, 9 × 2 is 18, ... Start with the students, then let them go ahead on their own.

Repeat with times tables for other multiplication facts.

What's Missing?

Today you're going to find two missing numbers in a series. Write a string of numbers, in order, with some numbers missing, on the overhead projector. Using a pencil as a pointer, indicate a blank space. ***Let's say what number is missing here. Tell how you know.***

Point to each blank space, having different students tell you about their thinking.

10,002; 10,003 . . .

Try these:

• 10,000; 10,001; ____; ____; 10,004

• 43,200; ____; ____; 43,203; 43,204

• 60,989; ____; 60,991; ____; 60,993

• 81,997; 81,998; 81,999; ____; ____

Convince Me!

Read this story problem to the class. ***Today 9 children are pasting pictures in a scrapbook. If each child pastes 15 pictures in the book, how many pictures will they paste in all?*** Engage the class in a Convince Me! discussion as explained on pages T6 to T12. **(135 pictures)**

True or False?

Today we are going to think about greater than and less than with fractions. Write $\frac{1}{2} > \frac{1}{4}$ on the overhead projector with the light off. Turn on the light and say, **Look at this number statement and be ready to say if it is true or false.** Let the students look for a few seconds, then say, **Is it true or false?** Repeat the activity with other fraction statements, some true and some false.

Try these:

- $\frac{1}{3} > \frac{1}{2}$ **(F)**
- $\frac{1}{4} > \frac{1}{8}$ **(T)**
- $\frac{1}{6} < \frac{1}{3}$ **(T)**
- $\frac{2}{3} < \frac{1}{2}$ **(F)**

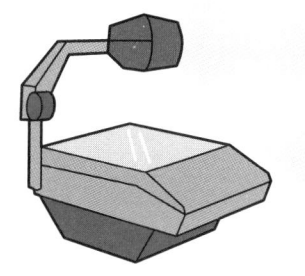

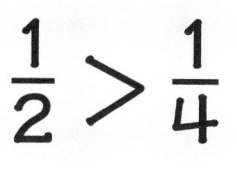

$$\frac{1}{2} > \frac{1}{4}$$

Topic: Fractions **Focus:** Comparing

Convince Me!

Ask the following question and let several students give answers. **_Which is greater, $\frac{2}{4}$ or $\frac{1}{2}$?_** Engage the class in a Convince Me! discussion as explained on pages T6 to T12.

Listen and Think

We're going to do some math in our heads. Listen closely, then we'll all say the answer together. Pause after saying the first two numbers, then continue with the last one. ***Ready?*** *3 × 4 + 12.* Have the class say the answer together. Begin saying the problems slowly, but increase the pace as you progress.

Try these:

- *50 − 10 × 2* (80)
- *16 + 4 ÷ 2* (10)
- *17 + 19 − 7* (29)

Twenty-four!

Convince Me!

Ask the following question and let several students give answers. ***Which is greater, $\frac{9}{9}$ or $\frac{10}{10}$?*** Engage the class in a Convince Me! discussion as explained on pages T6 to T12.

Let's play the **How Much?** *game again. Listen closely because you are going to add and take away amounts of money in your heads.*
Name the following coins slowly and have the class say the final value.

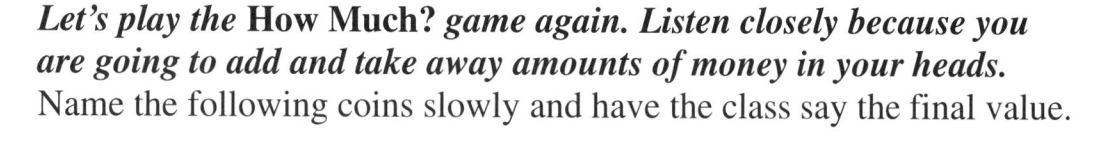

Try these:

- *dime, take away nickel, dime, dime, penny* ($0.26)

- *quarter, take away dime, nickel, nickel, penny* ($0.26)

- *quarter, quarter, take away dime, take away nickel, penny, penny* ($0.37)

- *half dollar, take away quarter, dime, dime, take away nickel* ($0.40)

Convince Me!

Write the following problems on the chalkboard one at a time. Engage the class in a Convince Me! discussion as explained on pages T6 to T12.

- $\begin{array}{r} 121 \\ -\ \ 99 \end{array}$ **(22)**

- $100 \div 20 =$ **(5)**

- $\begin{array}{r} 156 \\ +\ 104 \end{array}$ **(260)**

- $\begin{array}{r} 14 \\ \times\ \ \ 7 \end{array}$ **(98)**

- $\begin{array}{r} 20 \\ \times\ 10 \end{array}$ **(200)**

- $\begin{array}{r} 314 \\ +\ 619 \end{array}$ **(933)**

- $250 \div 50 =$ **(5)**

- $\begin{array}{r} 524 \\ -\ 125 \end{array}$ **(399)**

Topic: Discussions   **Focus:** Computation strategies

Miniboard day again! Put transparent Base Ten Blocks on the overhead projector to show 2 rows of 13. Turn on the light and say, *Look at these blocks and think of the multiplication problem they show. Write the equation that shows the problem and then write the answer.* On your signal, the students should show their Miniboards. (**2 × 13 = 26**)

Try these:

* 2 rows with 18 in each row (**2 × 18 = 36**)

* 2 rows with 17 in each row (**2 × 17 = 34**)

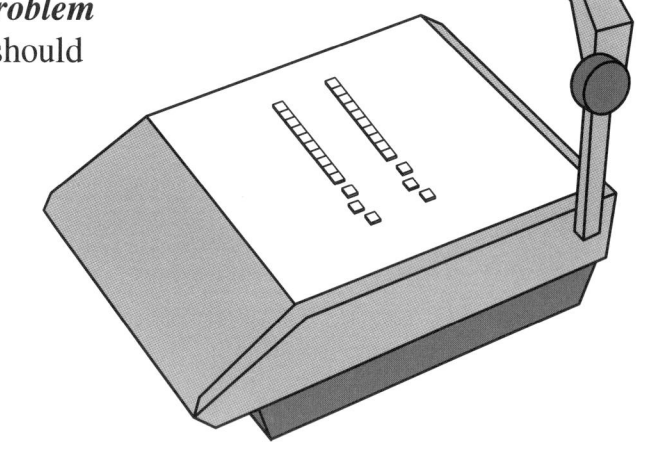

Convince Me!

Ask the following question and let several students give answers. ***Which is greater, $\frac{1}{4}$ of 12 or $\frac{1}{2}$ of 10?*** Engage the class in a Convince Me! discussion as explained on pages T6 to T12.

Topic: Discussions   **Focus:** Computation strategies, fractions

132 ◆ 10,000 More

It's a Miniboard day! You're going to write the number that is 10,000 more than the number I write. Turn on the overhead projector and write a number on it. **Write the number that is 10,000 more than this one. Write it on your Miniboards.** On your signal, have the class show their Miniboards.

Try these:

- 13,000; 43,000; 39,001

- 18,209; 19,120; 17,891

- 62,034; 74,961; 41,359

For a challenge, have the class write the numbers that are 10,000 less than the ones you write.

Topic: Place value   **Focus:** Writing numbers

Convince Me!

Read this story problem to the class. ***Geraldo has 56 shoeboxes.
How many shoes could he put in the boxes, if he put one pair
in each box?*** Engage the class in a Convince Me! discussion as
explained on pages T6 to T12. (**112**)

Write It Right

It's a Miniboard day again! You're going to write numbers putting the correct greater than or less than signs between them. Write 684 481 > < on the overhead projector. *Copy these two numbers on your Miniboards and then write the correct sign between them.* On your signal, the students should show their Miniboards.

684>481

Try these:

- 329   937 (<)

- 104   189 (<)

- 6091   9061 (<)

- 1110   1010 (>)

Topic: Sequencing numbers, 100 to 10,000   **Focus:** Writing greater than, less than symbols

135 Convince Me!

Ask the following questions as you write the numbers on the chalkboard. Let several students give answers. Engage the class in a Convince Me! discussion as explained on pages T6 to T12.

- *If $2 \div 4 = \frac{1}{2}$, why does the calculator show the answer as 0.5?*

- *If $1 \div 8 = \frac{1}{8}$, why does the calculator show the answer as 0.125?*

Topic: Discussions   **Focus:** Computation strategies, fractions

Which Doesn't Belong?

Let's look at some shapes. I'll put 3 Polygon Tile shapes on the overhead projector. You tell me which one doesn't belong with the rest. Ready? Put a square, a triangle, and a rectangle on the overhead. Ask, ***Which doesn't belong? Why?*** The class should say all the shapes' names after they have identified the one that doesn't belong.

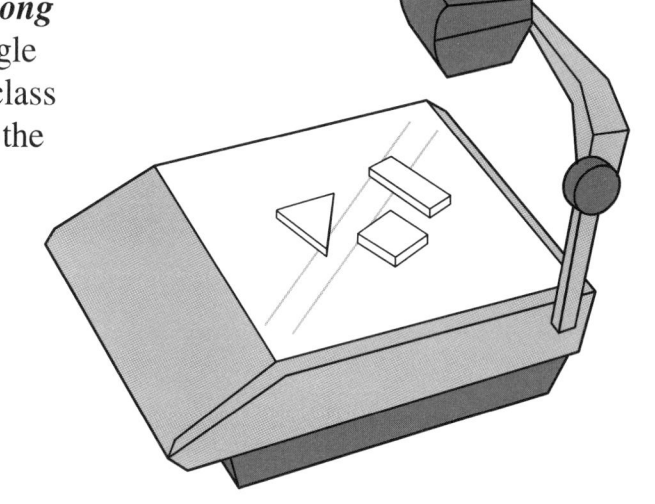

Try these:

• Triangle, another triangle, octagon

• Pentagon, parallelogram, rhombus

• Hexagon, octagon, another hexagon

• Rhombus, heptagon, square

Topic: Geometric shapes   **Focus:** Identifying shapes

Convince Me!

Write the following problems on the chalkboard one at a time.
Engage the class in a Convince Me! discussion as explained on
pages T6 to T12.

- $\begin{array}{r} 175 \\ + 275 \\ \hline \end{array}$ **(450)**

- $\begin{array}{r} 360 \\ + 189 \\ \hline \end{array}$ **(549)**

- $100 \div 25 =$ **(4)**

- $\begin{array}{r} 10 \\ \times \quad 18 \\ \hline \end{array}$ **(180)**

- $\begin{array}{r} 100 \\ \times \quad 5 \\ \hline \end{array}$ **(500)**

- $600 \div 6 =$ **(100)**

- $\begin{array}{r} 130 \\ \times \quad 10 \\ \hline \end{array}$ **(1300)**

- $\begin{array}{r} 316 \\ - 280 \\ \hline \end{array}$ **(36)**

Topic: Discussions   **Focus:** Computation strategies

Let's practice writing our numbers again. I'll say some numbers and you write them as neatly as you can on your paper. Afterwards we'll read them all together. Are you ready? Say the following numbers slowly, giving the students time to write them. After the students have finished, read the numbers aloud with them.

Try these:

- 10,702; 13,372; 15,555

- 72,306; 33,318; 25,800

- 101,312; 570,236; 169,198

139 ◆ **Convince Me!**

Read this story problem to the class. ***Maria counted 122 girls at the school picnic. Harry counted 137 boys. How many more boys than girls were at the picnic?*** Engage the class in a Convince Me! discussion as explained on pages T6 to T12. **(15)**

Topic: Discussions   **Focus:** Computation strategies

Answers

1. *Write the number I say: eight hundred sixty thousand, four hundred thirty-six.* **860,436**

2. [Write: 6871 ____ 8671, $<$ $>$] *Write the correct sign between the numbers.* **$<$**

3. [Write: 74,996; 74,997; 74,998] *Write the next two numbers.* **74,999; 75,000**

4. [Write: $\frac{2}{3} < \frac{1}{2}$] *Is this statement true or false?* **false**

5. [Write: 18,791] *Write the number that is ten thousand greater.* **28,791**

6. [Write: $\frac{5}{2}$] *Write a different name for this fraction.* **$2\frac{1}{2}$**

7. [Centimeter ruler: Draw a 6 centimeter line.] *How long is the line?* **6 cm**

8. [Polygon Tiles: triangle, rhombus, square] *Circle the shape that is not a quadrilateral.* **triangle**

9. [Rainbow Cubes: 2 rows of 16 each] *Write the multiplication equation the blocks show.* **$2 \times 16 = 32$**

For Verbal Response

10. *Say the 8's multiplication facts from 8 $\times$ 0 to 8 $\times$ 10.*

Two Names for One

Time for Miniboards! You're going to write two names for one fraction. Use transparent and opaque Fraction Circles on the overhead projector to show the fraction. Put on one whole transparent region, covered by 4 transparent fourths, and another opaque $\frac{1}{4}$ piece beside it. Turn on the light and say, *Write two different names for this fraction.* After giving students time to write, ask, *Who can tell one name for this fraction? Who knows another name for the same fraction?* On your signal, the students should show their Miniboards.

Try these:

- $\frac{6}{5}$ $\left(1\frac{1}{5}\right)$
- $\frac{11}{8}$ $\left(1\frac{3}{8}\right)$

- $\frac{5}{3}$ $\left(1\frac{2}{3}\right)$
- $\frac{9}{6}$ $\left(1\frac{1}{2} \text{ or } 1\frac{3}{6}\right)$

Topic: Fractions **Focus:** Naming mixed numbers

What Could They Be?

It's a Miniboard day! Use transparent Fraction Circles. With the overhead projector light on, put a $\frac{1}{2}$ piece on a whole region of the Fraction Circles. Ask the students to name the piece. Then turn the light off, remove the $\frac{1}{2}$ piece, and say, ***Suppose I cover the $\frac{1}{2}$ area with two pieces that are the same. What could they be? Write the fraction on your Miniboards.*** Then turn on the light to verify the answer. Next put 3 sixths on the $\frac{1}{2}$ area in the same way. On your signal, the class should show their Miniboards.

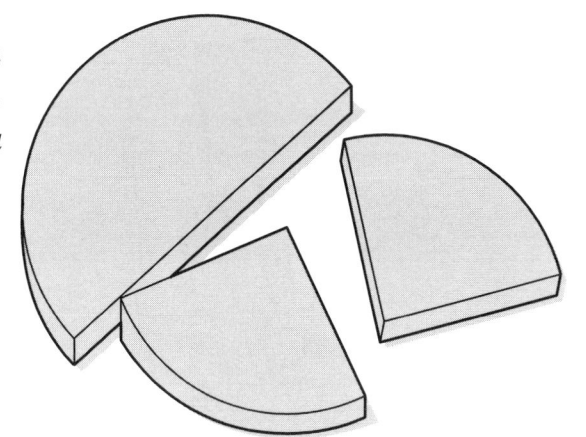

Try these:

- Cover $\frac{1}{4}$ area with $\frac{2}{8}$, with $\frac{3}{12}$

- Cover $\frac{4}{5}$ area with $\frac{8}{10}$

- Cover $\frac{1}{3}$ area with $\frac{2}{6}$, with $\frac{4}{12}$

Topic: Fractions   **Focus:** Naming equivalent parts

(143) Convince Me!

Write the following problems on the chalkboard one at a time.
Engage the class in a Convince Me! discussion as explained on
pages T6 to T12.

-
$$\begin{array}{r} 435 \\ +\ 282 \end{array} \quad \textbf{(717)}$$

-
$$\begin{array}{r} 4299 \\ -\ 119 \end{array} \quad \textbf{(4180)}$$

- $100 \div 100 = \textbf{(1)}$

-
$$\begin{array}{r} 26 \\ \times\ 6 \end{array} \quad \textbf{(156)}$$

-
$$\begin{array}{r} 999 \\ +\ 861 \end{array} \quad \textbf{(1860)}$$

-
$$\begin{array}{r} 526 \\ -\ 139 \end{array} \quad \textbf{(387)}$$

-
$$\begin{array}{r} 9 \\ \times\ 9 \end{array} \quad \textbf{(81)}$$

- $63 \div 7 = \textbf{(9)}$

Topic: Discussions **Focus:** Computation strategies

Which Doesn't Belong?

Let's look at some shapes again. I'll put 3 Polygon Tile shapes on the overhead projector. You tell me which one doesn't belong with the rest. Ready? Put a square, an equilateral triangle (**32**) and a trapezoid (**39**) on the overhead. Ask, *Which doesn't belong? Why?* The class should say all the shapes' names after they have identified the one that doesn't belong.

Try these:

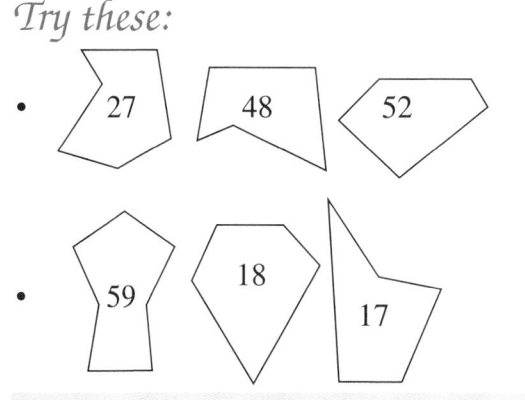

- 27   48   52

- 59   18   17

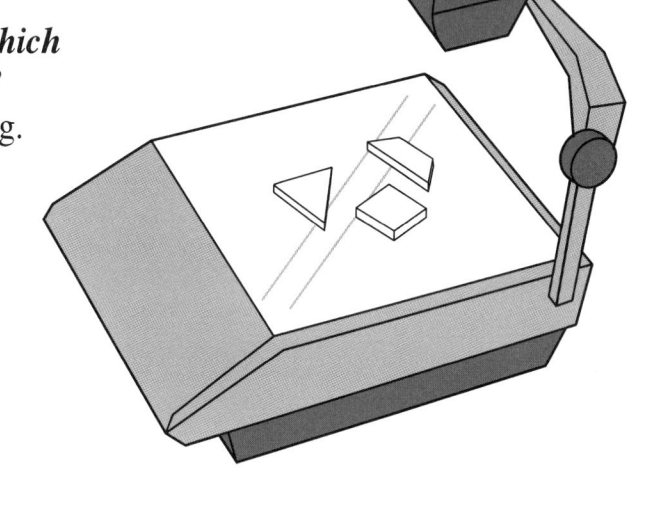

Topic: Geometric shapes

Focus: Identifying shapes

Ask the following question and let several students give answers. **Which is greater, $\frac{1}{3}$ of 12 or $\frac{1}{4}$ of 8?** Engage the class in a Convince Me! discussion as explained on pages T6 to T12. ($\frac{1}{3}$ of 12)

How Much Is Hidden?

Let's play a coin game. I'll put some coins on the overhead projector and tell you their total value. Then I'll cover some of them and you tell me what coins could be hiding. Put transparent coins, 1 quarter, 2 dimes, 2 nickels, and 3 pennies, on the overhead with the light off. Say, ***These coins are worth fifty-eight cents.*** Cover 1 dime, 1 nickel, and 2 pennies. Turn the light on and ask the students to say what coins you could be hiding.

After the students have guessed correctly, hide a different set of coins.

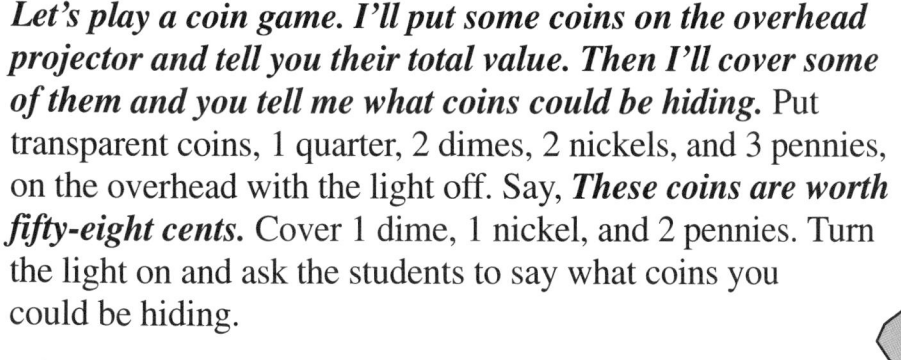

Topic: Mental arithmetic   **Focus:** Adding and subtracting money

Convince Me!

Ask the following questions. Engage the class in a Convince Me! discussion as explained on pages T6 to T12.

- *There are 52 weeks in 1 year. How many weeks are there in 5 years?* (260)

- *There are 366 days in a Leap Year. How many days are there in 2 Leap Years?* (732)

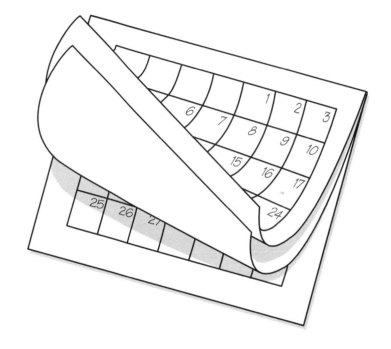

Topic: Discussions   **Focus:** Computation strategies, time   MathLand®: Grade Four
© Creative Publications   **147**

Billions and Millions

Today you're going to read numbers in the millions and in the billions without any help from cards. Write the number 264,481,199 on the chalkboard. Read it with the students. *Two hundred sixty-four million, four hundred eighty-one thousand, one hundred ninety-nine.* Let various students take turns saying the number by themselves.

Then write another number, this time in the billions, for the class to read. Repeat, writing other large numbers.

264, 481, 199

Convince Me!

Write the following problems on the chalkboard one at a time.
Engage the class in a Convince Me! discussion as explained on
pages T6 to T12.

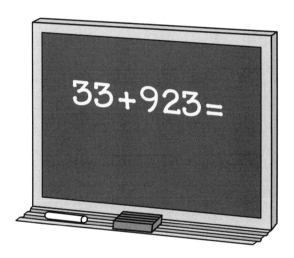

- $33 + 923 =$ **(956)**

- $250 \div 25 =$ **(10)**

- $\begin{array}{r} 423 \\ - \quad 24 \end{array}$ **(399)**

- $\begin{array}{r} 682 \\ - \quad 79 \end{array}$ **(603)**

- $\begin{array}{r} 24 \\ \times \quad 4 \end{array}$ **(96)**

- $\begin{array}{r} 123 \\ + 796 \end{array}$ **(919)**

- $\begin{array}{r} 122 \\ - 102 \end{array}$ **(20)**

- $\begin{array}{r} 18 \\ \times \quad 6 \end{array}$ **(108)**

Topic: Discussions   **Focus:** Computation strategies

Hidden Blocks

It's a Miniboard day! Put these transparent Base Ten Blocks on the overhead projector: 2 hundreds blocks, 3 tens blocks, and 4 ones blocks. Cover 1 hundreds block, 2 tens blocks, and 3 ones blocks with a card. Turn on the light and say, **These blocks show 234 in all.** Write 234 on the overhead. **However, I've covered some of them. Make a drawing on your Miniboards of the covered blocks.** Wait until most of the students are finished, then ask one student to name the hidden blocks.

Try the activity again, this time covering different blocks.

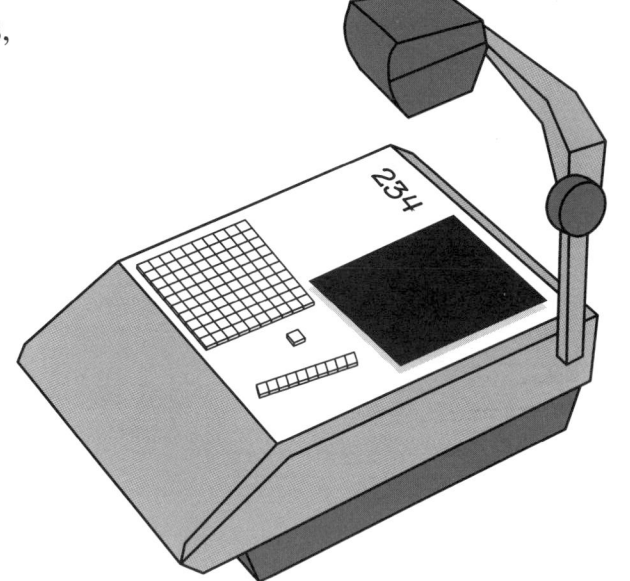

234

Topic: Problems
Focus: Addition

Convince Me!

Ask the following question and let several students give answers. ***Which is greater, $\frac{1}{3}$ of 9 or $\frac{1}{3}$ of 12?*** Engage the class in a Convince Me! discussion as explained on pages T6 to T12. ($\frac{1}{3}$ **of 12**)

It's a Miniboard day again! You're going to write numbers putting the correct greater than or less than signs between them. Write 31,468 46,831 > < on the overhead projector. *Copy these two numbers on your Miniboards and then write the correct sign between them.* On your signal, the students should show their Miniboards.

Try these:

- 70,329   92,307 (<)

- 10,004   9989 (>)

- 60,691   56,906 (>)

- 10,111   11,000 (<)

Convince Me!

Draw on the chalkboard a line that is 1 yard long. Mark it off in 3 feet. Ask the following questions. Engage the class in a Convince Me! discussion as explained on pages T6 to T12.

- *There are 3 feet in 1 yard. How many feet are there in 3 yards?* **(9 feet)**

- *There are 12 inches in 1 foot. How many inches are there in 1 yard?* **(36 inches)**

- *How many feet are there in 24 inches?* **(2 feet)**

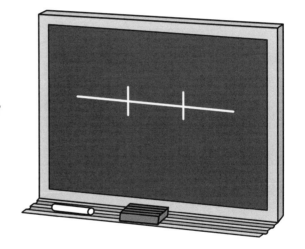

Topic: Discussions   **Focus:** Computation strategies, measurement

Which Divide Evenly?

It's a Miniboard day again! Look at these division equations. Write them on your Miniboards. Then raise your hand when you find the equation that has an answer with a remainder. We'll all say that equation together. Write on the overhead projector: 60 ÷ 15 = _____; 32 ÷ 6 = _____; 36 ÷ 6 = _____; 35 ÷ 7 = _____. Give the students time to think about the equations, and wait until most have raised their hands.

Repeat with the following equations: 28 ÷ 13 = _____; 35 ÷ 5 = _____; 27 ÷ 9 = _____; 20 ÷ 4 = _____;

Topic: Number facts   **Focus:** Division

Convince Me!

Ask the following questions, one at a time. Engage the class in a Convince Me! discussion as explained on pages T6 to T12.

- *Luz has 16 cookies and $\frac{1}{4}$ of them are broken. How many cookies are broken?* (4)

- *Ann has 20 boxes and only $\frac{1}{5}$ of them have lids. How many boxes have lids?* (4)

- *Harpreet has 18 baseball cards and $\frac{1}{3}$ of them are torn. How many cards are torn?* (6)

Topic: Discussions   **Focus:** Computation strategies, fractions

Is It Greater?

It's Miniboard time! Get ready for some fraction problems. You're going to write some fractions, putting the correct greater than or less than sign between them. Write $\frac{1}{6}$ $\frac{1}{3}$ $<$ $>$ on the overhead projector. *Copy these two fractions on your Miniboards and then write the correct sign between them.* On your signal, the students should show their Miniboards.

Try these:

- $\frac{2}{3}$ $\frac{1}{2}$ $(>)$
- $\frac{3}{4}$ $\frac{2}{3}$ $(>)$
- $\frac{1}{4}$ $\frac{1}{3}$ $(<)$
- $\frac{1}{2}$ $\frac{3}{4}$ $(<)$
- $\frac{3}{6}$ $\frac{3}{5}$ $(<)$

Topic: Fractions   **Focus:** Writing greater than, less than symbols

Convince Me!

Read this story problem to the class. ***Lupe had 4 candy bars. She divided each one into 8 equal pieces and gave 1 piece to each student in her class. How many students got $\frac{1}{8}$ of a candy bar?*** Engage the class in a Convince Me! discussion as explained on pages T6 to T12. **(32)**

How Long?

It's Miniboard and measurement time again! Put a transparent inch ruler on the overhead projector. Draw a line that is exactly $4\frac{1}{2}$ inches long. Ask the students to write on their Miniboards how long the line is. Mark off other lines in inch lengths and have the students write those lengths. On your signal, have the students show their Miniboards.

Try these:

- $5\frac{1}{2}$ inches

- $2\frac{1}{4}$ inches

- $3\frac{3}{4}$ inches

Convince Me!

Write the following problems on the chalkboard one at a time. Engage the class in a Convince Me! discussion as explained on pages T6 to T12.

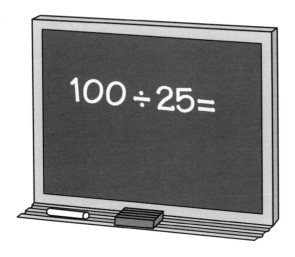

- 100 ÷ 25 = **(4)**

- 6113
  + 983   **(7096)**

- 312
  − 215   **(97)**

- 10
  × 10   **(100)**

- 469
  + 378   **(847)**

- 519
  − 420   **(99)**

- 200 ÷ 50 = **(4)**

- 13
  × 4   **(52)**

Topic: Discussions   **Focus:** Computation strategies

Answers

1. [Write: 42,579 ____ 57, 942] *Write the correct greater than/less than sign.*
$<$

2. [Write: $\frac{3}{6}$ ____ $\frac{3}{5}$] *Write the correct greater than/less than sign.*
$<$

3. [Fraction Circles: $\frac{1}{2}$ piece on a whole] *What fraction piece can you use 3 of to cover $\frac{1}{2}$?*
$\frac{1}{6}$

4. *Sam has 50¢. He has 6 coins. Draw one group of coins he could have.*
vary

5. [Write: 40 ÷ 8 = ____; 30 ÷ 15 = ____, 42 ÷ 9 = ____, 49 ÷ 7 = ____]
Which has an answer with a remainder?
42 ÷ 9

6. [Inch Ruler: Draw $6\frac{1}{2}$ inch line.] *Write the length of this line.*
$6\frac{1}{2}$ **in.**

7. *Write the money amount I say: thirty-four dollars and six cents.*
$34.06

8. [Write: $\frac{9}{6}$] *Write another name for this fraction.*
$1\frac{1}{2}$ **or** $1\frac{3}{6}$

9. [Base Ten Blocks: 2 hundreds, 4 tens, 2 ones] *Write the number the blocks show.*
242

10. *Write the number for seventeen billion, five thousand.*
17,000,005,000

Read this story problem to the class. *It's Helena's birthday! She brought 84 treats to school. She wants to give an equal number to each of the other 28 students in her class. How many treats will each person get?* Engage the class in a Convince Me! discussion as explained on pages T6 to T12. **(3)**

What Could They Be?

It's a Miniboard day! Time to think about fractions again.
With the overhead projector light on, put a $\frac{1}{6}$ piece on a whole region of the Fraction Circles. Ask the students to name the piece. Then turn the light off, remove the $\frac{1}{6}$ piece, and say, ***Suppose I cover the $\frac{1}{6}$ area with two pieces that are the same. What could they be? Write that fraction on your Miniboards.*** Then turn on the light to verify the answer. On your signal, the class should show their Miniboards. ($\frac{2}{12}$)

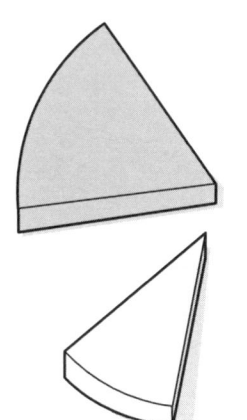

Try these:

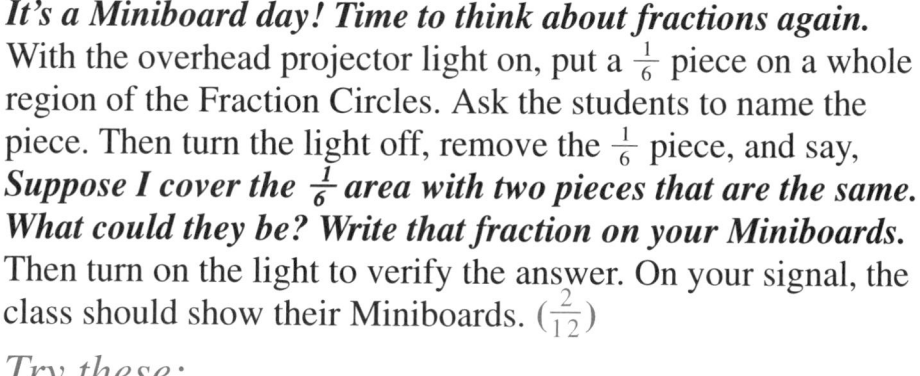

- Cover $\frac{2}{3}$ area with $\frac{4}{6}$, with $\frac{8}{12}$

- Cover $\frac{2}{5}$ area with $\frac{4}{10}$

- Cover $\frac{3}{4}$ area with $\frac{6}{8}$, with $\frac{9}{12}$

Convince Me!

Write the following problems on the chalkboard one at a time.
Engage the class in a Convince Me! discussion as explained on
pages T6 to T12.

- 301
  − 222   (79)

- 60 ÷ 15 = (4)

- 100
  × 23   (2300)

- 15
  × 5   (75)

- 800
  − 725   (75)

- 900
  + 1000   (1900)

- 827
  + 492   (1319)

- 800 ÷ 80 = (10)

Topic: Discussions   **Focus:** Computation strategies

Hidden Blocks

It's a Miniboard day! Put these transparent Base Ten Blocks on the overhead projector: 3 hundreds blocks, 5 tens blocks, and 5 ones blocks. Cover 1 hundreds block, 4 tens blocks, and 2 ones blocks with a card. Turn on the light and say, *These blocks show 355 in all.* Write 355 on the overhead. *However, I've covered some of them. Make a drawing on your Miniboards of the covered blocks.* Wait until most of the students are finished, then ask one student to name the hidden blocks.

Try the activity again, this time covering different blocks.

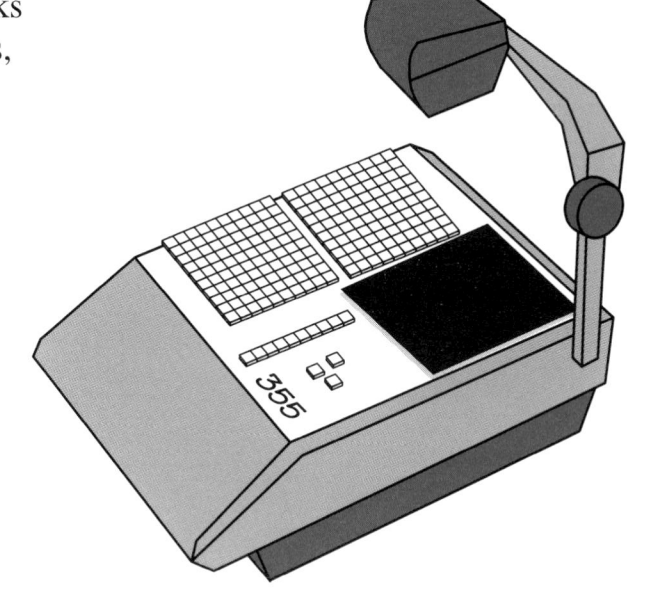

Convince Me!

Read this story problem to the class. *Max had 100 comic books. He divided them into 10 piles and then began to read one pile a week. How many comic books did he read each week?* Engage the class in a Convince Me! discussion as explained on pages T6 to T12. **(10)**

Topic: Discussions   **Focus:** Computation strategies

What Comes Before?

Let's play the **What Comes Before?** *game. I'll say a number and then you say the number that comes just before it.* Say random numbers greater than 10,000 and have the class say the previous number.

Try these:

- **20,421** (20,420)

- **48,690** (48,689)

- **31,900** (31,899)

- **100,000** (99,999)

Topic: Sequencing numbers, greater than 10,000   **Focus:** Naming the previous number

Convince Me!

Read this story problem to the class. *Sara has saved 364 coupons. She needs 520 in all so she can send for a prize. How many more coupons does she need to save?* Engage the class in a Convince Me! discussion as explained on pages T6 to T12. **(156)**

Topic: Discussions   **Focus:** Computation strategies

Hidden Blocks

Are you ready for a tricky problem today? Get out your Miniboards! Put these transparent Base Ten Blocks on the overhead projector: 2 hundreds blocks, 3 tens blocks, and 11 ones blocks. Cover 1 hundreds block, 2 tens blocks, and 3 ones blocks with a card. Turn on the light and say, *These blocks show 241 in all.* Write 241 on the overhead. *However, I've covered some of them. Make a drawing on your Miniboards of the covered blocks.* Wait until most of the students are finished, then ask one student to name the hidden blocks.

Try the activity again, this time covering different blocks.

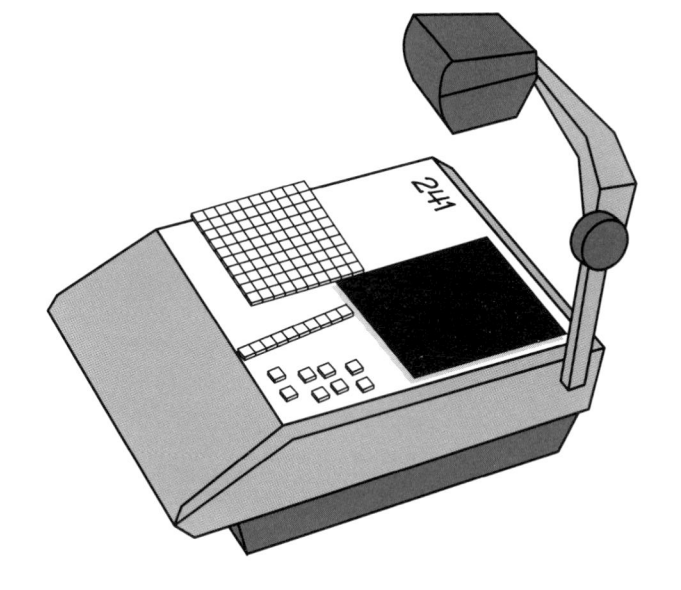

Topic: Problems

Focus: Addition

Convince Me!

Write the following problems on the chalkboard one at a time. Engage the class in a Convince Me! discussion as explained on pages T6 to T12.

- 1000 ÷ 500 = **(2)**

-     195
    + 728   **(923)**

-   2714
    − 417   **(2297)**

-     25
    × 20   **(500)**

-     289
    + 946   **(1235)**

-     811
    − 748   **(63)**

- 144 ÷ 12 = **(12)**

-      8
    × 7   **(56)**

Answers

1. *Write the number I say: 77,002* — 77,002

2. [Write: 49,740] *Write the number that comes just before.* — 49,739

3. [Fraction Circles: 6 sixths on a whole; 1 other sixth] *Write two names for this fraction.* — $\frac{7}{6}, 1\frac{1}{6}$

4. [9 quarters. Cover 2.] *I have $2.25 in all. What 2 coins are covered?* — 2 quarters

5. [Write: 6478 − 2359] *Name two numbers the answer falls between.* — vary

6. *How many feet in 24 inches?* — 2 feet

7. [Base Ten Blocks: 3 hundreds, 1 ten, 8 ones.] *Draw the additional blocks needed to show 530 in all.* — sketch 212

8. *Draw a picture of one way to show 5 × 13.* — Sketch

9. [Fraction Circles: 2 fifths] *What fraction piece can you use 4 of to cover $\frac{2}{5}$?* — $\frac{1}{10}$

10. [Polygon Tiles: pentagon (#16), parallelogram (#8), rhombus (#7)] *Draw the shape that does not belong. Tell why.* — vary